Of Substance

A Memoir

KAMERON PARKIN

First Edition

PAGE PUBLISHING, INC.
Conneaut Lake, PA

First originally published by Page Publishing 2020

ISBN 978-1-64334-870-4 (pbk)
ISBN 978-1-64334-873-5 (digital)

Printed in the United States of America

To those who gave me the life story

To those who empowered me to write it

To Kimmy
To Elizabeth
To Charlotte

I hope you never read this.

Acknowledgments

Perspective is like DNA.

Unique to every human born into this world, one experience will never be identical to two individuals.

This book contains my story. This book is written from my individual perspective. Others may not have the same perspective as me, but that's okay. We all experience each other in different ways.

Life is beautiful. Life is painful, life hurts, and life brings joy. If you happen to be one of those lucky people to be included in this book, I invite you to read the whole thing. See how it ends. Give it a chance. If you disagree with my words, I totally support your right to disagree with me. Your individual perspective is different. I love you for it. We are all entitled to our own life.

To all others—I love my life and everyone in it. I've gone through challenges in my life, but they made me into who I am today. I like who I am today. My wife likes who I am today. Everyone in my life who truly loves and knows me does as well.

Now, to the people that will never speak to me again—and there probably will be a few. Here's my last word. I will always be here to come back to. I love you.

Kameron Michael Parkin
December 2018, Tuesday, 11:30 a.m.

I took the ten-year-old iMac out of the box Pop-Pop had FedExed to me. Everything was labeled. Dad was obsessed with labels. The keyboard was labeled. The bottom of the computer was labeled. After five minutes of waiting and silent prayer, the computer booted. I clicked on the password field, entering Dad's name according to the label on the back of the keyboard: "michael parkin."

Success. I was into the account. I waited the entire month of November for that Pandora's box to arrive from Utah. I opened the web browser. The most recent Google queries confirmed my suspicions:

> "Statute of limitations for manslaughter."
> "Homicide sentences."
> "Trauma that doesn't show up on autopsy."

An obituary sat open on the desktop. According to the modified date of the document, my father's obituary was the last thing the computer was used for. I ripped the computer's power supply cable from the wall.

Murder hit me.

Chapter 1

Red Lake

I was fourteen years old when I saw a naked woman for the first time. Her face was red. She was covered in blood. It took a moment for me to realize she was my mother.

2009

I opened the front door of my home, knowing that the person to greet me would be my refrigerator. A good novel or television would keep me occupied until one of my parents got home.

That day was different. I was overwhelmed with a sharp smell of iron. I didn't know where the smell was coming from. Both of my parents should have been at work, but I could hear the faucets running somewhere upstairs.

I dropped my backpack and walked up the stairs to see who was home. With each step I climbed, the scent grew stronger. The master bedroom door was ajar. I walked through the doorway; the room was empty. I continued in pursuit of the smell. The air from the master bathroom collided with my face. Humid and metallic, like wet hammers, the scent struck my lungs with every breath. A large pool of blood lay spilled on the beige tile floor, like a red lake. The blood collected on the floor, as if from a brook. The lake appeared to be fed by a source located in the shower. My gut told me that I was standing in the scene of fatal trauma. Not a soul was around.

In shock, I began to panic. Fear set in that someone had been killed. So much blood covered the floors. The sight overtook my senses.

I turned around and saw my mother. She staggered into the bedroom, naked. Disoriented, my mother stood there. She seemed to stare through me as if I were a ghost. Confounded by what I saw, I tried to grapple with my reaction. Fight or flight held me captive at the foot of her bed.

Blood seeped down from Mom's nose and mouth as she gagged and fought for breath. As she walked toward me, she left a trail of blood before she collapsed on the bed. That was the day I lost my childhood.

The starter motor in my head nearly burned out. I had to move, but my mind just wouldn't turn over. I heard different words in my thoughts—muffled words. Ideas on the cusp of igniting. But I just could not move. I knew I needed something. What, what did I need? Mom was lying on the bed. She looked distant. My mind was cranking, desperate to start up to get to a steady idle. I strained to hear.

Phone...Phone... Once more, my brain squealed in protest. *Ignition.* I started thinking again. *Phone.* I patted my front pocket. I needed to call for help. I broke away from the scene.

I'd received my first cell phone for my fourteenth birthday. My silver Motorola Razr was a way for instant communication for days like that day.

I ran down the stairs and grabbed the cell phone out of my backpack. Instead of calling 911, I called Dad.

"Dad. You need to come home now."

"Huh? Everything all right?"

"*No.* That's why I'm calling you! It's Mom. OD'd. Just got home and she passed out on the bed. There's blood. A lot of blood. Hurry!"

"Okay, I'll be right there. Hang on. Do we need to call an ambulance?"

"No, I don't think so. Just get here!"

Dad's work was located twenty minutes south of our house.

I knew the number for poison control, but I already knew what they'd tell me.

Dad walked in the front door in the hall downstairs. I called to him from Mom's room. "We're up here!"

As he came up the stairs, he called out to me. "Is she okay?" Before I could reply, he reached the bedroom.

With a moment of eye contact, one glance exchanged between father and son communicated that day was to be, yet another day that I would suppress in my memory. For the sake of my own sanity, memories like those needed to go down to reside very deep inside my mind.

He kept asking if I was okay. "Kameron, are you okay? We're going to deal with this. Mom is gonna be fine. You did great helping her."

I figured he had enough to deal with already. "I'm fine. Don't worry about it. Let's just get her to the hospital."

After we got Mom looking like she was halfway normal, Dad and I loaded her into the front seat of the car. We managed to buckle Mom up before she passed out again.

"About the nose," Dad said. "I'm thinking that she tripped in the garage. Hit the deep freezer. Sound good?"

"I'd believe it. But, Dad, how are we going to explain the disorientation? If they do a tox screen? How do you want to deal with that?"

Dad educated me. "The best lies have a hint of truth, Kam. I am almost certain that the doctors will do a toxicology screen. Did you actually see Mom take anything?"

"Uh, no. This is how she was when I first saw her." I could see where he was going.

"Exactly. You found her like that."

For someone who, up until a year ago, had given me a very honest upbringing, Dad seemed skilled at bending truth.

"Okay. Let's just pray the doctors think it's a nose bleed and a concussion."

Dad appeared worried.

Vivid alibis become second nature to fourteen-year-olds. Most often the talent is acquired due to concealing their bad deeds from parents. For me, my exceptional lying skills came from a desire to harness control of my life. Such possession is not considered commonplace in "the system." For me it was CPS and an unknown future *or* freedom.

I knew what I wanted. Giving up a piece of my integrity was the price. Self-taught sociopathy and detachment were the vehicle. I knew if I was going to survive my childhood, I would have to drive that vehicle into the ground.

2018
July 21, Saturday, 2:36 a.m.

When the phone rings at two thirty in the morning, one needs to prepare for bad news. The last time my father's husband, Mike Burton, had a reason to call in the middle of the night, he informed me that my father was in the psych ward due to a suicide attempt. Getting a call from Mike Burton was never a pleasure. This time was no different. I became lucid.

"Hi, Mike. What's up?"

"I've got some really bad news." Though I was half-asleep, I had a feeling that this was the phone call I knew would come someday.

"I'm calling because your father is in a coma."

"What?"

Yep. Indeed, this was the call.

"Kameron, Your Father's in a coma. He may never wake up."

"How? Why?" I replied, trying to look for anything that would tie me to reality. It couldn't be true, could it?

Mike Burton continued. "He was in an accident. He was just fine. Then the next minute, he was on the floor. He just fell off the barstool here at home. I called 911, and he has been in a coma since it happened. The doctor says it was an aneurysm."

I responded before I grasped the concept. I couldn't take any more conversation. "Okay, I'm kinda in shock. I'll call you back in a bit."

I told Kimmy, my wife, about the latest episode to air in my family's soap opera. With a Google search on the subject, I knew I would never be able to talk to my father again. When the sun was up, I attempted to go about my day as normal. It didn't work.

Because Mike Burton and Dad had been married at the time, neither my grandparents nor I were next of kin. The person making executive decisions concerning the fate of my father was the manic-depressive alcoholic that Dad fled to when he couldn't cope with his sexual orientation. When I needed my father the most, Mike Burton had always held him captive.

I received another call from Mike burton after the sun was up. He was already talking about final arrangements and turning off life support.

"Hey, Kam, we need to discuss next steps. Like how long we are going to continue life support. I know your dad. He wouldn't want to be kept alive artificially. I know its soon, but we need to talk about turning off the machines and final arrangements."

"Mike, hold on, I am coming out there as soon as I can. I'm going to be involved in this."

"Okay, when are you coming out, Kameron?"

"Right away, Michael. I will be there in the morning."

At the end of the phone call, I realized I needed to be in Utah ASAP, if I wanted to say goodbye to Dad. A ten-hour drive would put me in Utah at around 2:00 a.m.

Chapter 2

Double Life

2012

I was sixteen going on seventeen. My life was in two halves of a household. Every Friday my backpack was just a bit heavier. I would go home to a different bedroom than I spent the previous week in. Mom was in her new apartment, and my father lived in the house that he had rented for me and my mom when they separated.

The day my father moved Mom and me into that house, he defined "us" as my mother and me.

One Friday, my father introduced me to "Someone important." A man named Michael, like my dad. Mike Burton was a charismatic person—smooth and cunning. He could adapt his interests to anyone who he wanted to impress. Mike was so likable and perfect that everyone he met soon lost sight of how sleazy he was, right down to his core. At that moment, I realized that one of Mike Burton's main interests was Dad. Years of my suspicion evolved into reality. My dad was gay.

In my parents' divorce decree, a specific condition regarding custody was put into place. It stated, "Neither party shall permit the minor child to be in the presence of a significant other." This condition could revoke custody from either parent. It seemed like a big deal but not to my dad. I, however, knew that if my mother found out about my exposure to Mike Burton, the game was over for my dad. One hundred percent custody would go to my mother.

As I was coming to terms with this new gear in the delicate machine of my life, I tried to form a strategy by which my father could maintain custody. I learned early on to locate the exits as I walked into a room. There always had to be an escape route. I needed to know who or what was behind me, in front of me, and next to me.

Mike Burton was a giant barrier to my freedom. He was placed in front of my only means of escape. After talking with Dad, I found that Dad also knew that he was going against the divorce decree. Even though I didn't agree with what Dad was doing, I knew I had to appease him in order to keep control of my circumstances. Dad assured me that I would be safe, that he could manage everything.

When Mike Burton moved in with Dad, we went over house rules. The garage door was always to be closed, so nobody knew Mike Burton lived there. Dad and I needed one car. Mike Burton's Audi S4 was conspicuous, to say the least.

In the lease on the house, smoking was not permitted. Mike had to smoke outside. He lit up on the side of the house, which faced a new construction project that was not yet completed.

Of course, I was not allowed to tell anybody that Mike Burton lived with us. Nor was I to mention any other rules in the divorce decree that were broken, such as consumption of alcohol and marijuana.

After my first week with Dad, my mother picked me up at school. My week with her marked the beginning of my double life. I had to figure out a way to stay with dad full-time. Dad had identified several times that Mom was going downhill with her drug problem. He told me that If I wanted to, I would be able to stay with him full-time, rather than just every other week, per the custody arrangement.

2018
July 21, Saturday, 4:00 p.m.

I threw what I thought I needed into my trusty black duffel bag. I didn't pack a suit. I knew in the back of my mind I might need something formal. It was too difficult to pack a suit. Maybe if I didn't pack for a specific occasion, it wouldn't come.

I kissed Kimmy and put my duffel bag in the car. I looked around my Lexus RX300, dissatisfied with the messy SUV. Dad always traveled in pristine cars. He would not approve of the current state of the car that I'd be driving for seven hundred miles. I set my GPS to University of Utah Medical Center and drove off.

With a click of the garage door opener, I remembered a time when I had to familiarize myself with garage door mechanisms. My knowledge came out of necessity, in a time when I had to keep my mother from pressing charges against my father to get custody back from him.

Chapter 3

Criminal Magic

2012

I learned to drive a stick when I was seventeen. I was driving away from a crime scene. I just assaulted the man who owned the car. The assault was perhaps fatal. For a moment, I imagined what my life would be like if I didn't return.

Whenever I see a black Honda Accord, my blood curdles. My first car would have been my dad's 1999 two-door Honda Accord with a stereo that could be heard from a mile away.

I loved turning up the volume on the stereo as we'd drive away from the school parking lot.

On one particular day, Dad picked me up from school. We drove home to find, as usual, Mike was at home. I retreated to my room to watch television. That year happened to be the first time I'd been allowed to have a TV in my room. I figured Dad was bribing me because if I told anyone Mike was living with us, he would be violating a court order.

I fell asleep that evening but woke up to the sound of a bottle breaking. I'd heard it before. I knew the Skyy vodka bottle without even seeing it. The sounds put everything in context for me. It was the glass shattering against a granite countertop—the shards sprinkling on the tile floor in the kitchen told me what was going on, for

I'd heard them a dozen times before. Mike hit him. The yelp that my father made told me I needed to saddle up for another rodeo.

I got dressed and laced my shoes. I used tight-fitting running shoes. I needed to be nimble on those nights. I prepared to go out into the living room. I knew that braking on black ice would cost me my control over the situation. Traditional domestic violence was familiar. Traditional domestic violence was a dance between male and female, blade and chalice. Though it wasn't right, it had a certain balance. What Dad and Mike Burton had in their battles wasn't traditional by any definition. Without any estrogen to keep a smooth cadence, the excess testosterone in the Boyfriend-on-boyfriend battles was a force not easily contained.

I found them, yet again, in another quarrel. Mike Burton was trying to cope with a felony breaking and entering charge, one count of burglary, violation of a restraining order, and assault—all filed by his ex-wife. Those charges raised the stakes with my father's custody situation as well.

A boyfriend around a minor child is one thing. A violent felon would be a nail in my dad's coffin that would be very troublesome to remove.

As the fight escalated, their control diminished. Both men were as smashed as the shards of blue glass littering the floor around them. Assault was a sport that Mike Burton engaged in with extreme skill and precision. I decided it would be appropriate if he received a medal. At the very least, Mike deserved a certificate of mastery from the Utah County Department of Justice.

My father had all but passed out in the corner, crying, begging me to call the police.

Mike Burton turned his attention toward me. He charged. Mike would avoid an encounter with law enforcement at all costs. I was surprised that Mike Burton still had as much strength as he did. He was left-handed. I knew he grabbed with his right. I was ready for him.

I set up my counterattack before he executed his strategy. I caught his right fingers, twisted his arm, and pinned him on the ground. I punched him the same way I would punch any other of his kind—right in the nose. To my dismay, the inebriated shark did not swim away.

I got away from him and reached for the phone. He followed and grabbed it from me. On the kitchen island, like a manifestation from heaven, sat another bottle of vodka, half-empty. I took it. Like I was splitting wood, I aimed right for the top of his head. The bottle crashed against his skull. Vodka baptized his head and my arm. He lost consciousness.

I heard a car start in the garage. I looked in the corner where Dad had been sitting. During my encounter with Mike, Dad had woken up and fled the scene. I ran to the garage. My weeping father sat in his car. The garage door was still shut.

Dad shifted the car into reverse. Looking behind him, he floored the black Honda into the garage door, rolling out of the cavity and onto the driveway. A lone detached spoiler was the only thing left in its place.

I didn't know what to do. Mike was unconscious in the kitchen where I left him, so I decided to go out to the driveway to see if the sideshow began attracting attention.

The car stopped only after the bottom of the garage door took its toll. Scraping the paint off the roof and off the hood. The trunk spoiler was ripped off the back. The rear window was cracked, and the sunroof was smashed in. I could not get through the garage door to the car. I tore through the house and out the front door. A passing glance at Mike Burton gave me confirmation that he would not be any problem for me for the rest of the night.

That was the first time I had ever smashed a bottle over someone's head. I knew that people in movies always woke up after being "hit out of the park" by a glass bat, but this wasn't a movie. Or baseball. Or a game. For a fleeting moment, the words "tried as an adult" came to mind.

Though everything was occurring in slow motion, I didn't have time left on the clock to think about what would happen tomorrow. If there was a day that I would face a judge, I would tell them, "I knew he'd kill me."

I reached the front door. I opened it and looked at the driveway. The only source of light to pierce through darkness was the cracked tail lights. No one seemed to have witnessed what had transpired.

We didn't have anyone living in the houses next to us or across the street on that holiday weekend. I couldn't rely on that. If I was going to maintain my living situation with my dad, I needed some magic to make the scene I was about to witness disappear.

I hesitated as I peered around the corner. I summed up the damage. I knew I was going to need a wand much better and a top hat far bigger than what came with the magic set I received for my eighth birthday.

My dad was leaning over the steering wheel, crying. Glass from the sunroof littered his shirt. He was cursing and yelling "Why am I here?" at himself, Mike Burton, God, and the universe. It wasn't apparent at that moment whom he hated most.. Like a stubborn puppy to his kennel, I was able to lure Dad back into the house.

He limped up the steps and staggered down the hall to his bedroom. I took his shoes off and put Dad on his side. Alcohol and my father had a messy relationship. When binge drinking, projectile vomiting was inevitable.

I had Mike Burton waiting in the kitchen, passed out. I didn't need my dad aspirating to death on top of everything else. I made sure he wasn't lying on his back. After Tweedle Drunk and Tweedle Drunker were squared away, I went back out to the garage to come up with a magic spell to make all the evidence disappear.

My father's car had all but ripped the garage door off the track. I could tell the door was beyond repair. I had to get rid of it somehow. I grabbed some gloves in lieu of a magic wand. The door fell on the driveway and on to the lawn. I pulled it to the backyard, out of sight. That was a very important door. For Mike Burton, it stood between him and a felony. My father used the door to protect himself from losing custody as well as keeping his alimony and child support payments locked in. For me, the door concealed the biggest secret I had ever kept.

My small list of options was redacted by the absence of that door. If the police were coming, I figured I was already in cuffs. What difference would driving without a license make?

I went back into the house to retrieve the keys to Mike's Audi. To my dismay, the keys weren't on the hook by the door. I crept into the kitchen and found Mike Burton how I'd left him. I found the keys to his Audi S4, which we'd spent the last month concealing. He let out a grumble which would have scared me off, but tonight it meant that I wouldn't be tried for murder.

Overjoyed, I sneaked back out of the house and hit the manual release on the other garage door behind Mike's car. With as much caution as I could, I lifted the handle on the garage door

Panels disappeared up into the dark void of the ceiling. I hopped in the driver's seat of Mike's Audi. Apart from the prospect of a homicide conviction going off the table just minutes earlier, that was the only enjoyable moment of the night.

I started the car. I slipped the car into reverse and drove down the road a ways. No longer would the neighbors know a particular black Audi was there. I walked back to the house. I could see the lights were on in the bedroom. As I passed the sliding glass door in the kitchen, I could see Mike Burton had not moved from where I'd left him. I figured Dad had gotten up to vomit or relieve himself. Whatever had happened, I would have to clean up the mess tomorrow.

I walked back to the garage. The keys were still in the Honda's ignition. If it weren't dealt with soon, the dawn would expose the disaster that had taken place. As I started the car, I could hear crackling pieces of glass underneath the tires. The Honda rolled back through the opening, and I pulled it into the stall where Mike's Audi had been. The door lowered. Now hiding a different secret. I took a look at the front of the house and decided to leave the glass and other mess in the garage for the morning. I left a note on the inside garage door and waited the rest of the night in the park nearby.

In the morning, I got breakfast at a gas station near the park. I cased the house to see if there had been a development. By then, the time was almost noon. As I walked past the house again, I saw Mike

Burton standing in his boxers on the back deck having a Bloody Mary with his morning cigarette. I stood, crouched behind the fence, and watched. Later, Mike went into the garage. Instead of a smoke, in his hand was an ice pack. From behind the fence I was using for cover, I heard him say "What the fuck?" as he noticed the note I'd hung on the garage door. He read it went back inside. He'd had the sense to grab a robe when he picked up his car key.

He walked down the street to retrieve his vehicle. I noticed nobody in the neighborhood had seen him. Everything damning had disappeared as if by magic. The problem with alcoholism was that when one is blackout drunk, like my dad and Mike Burton were that night, memories of events disappear.

Abracadabra.

2018
July 21, Saturday, 4:30 p.m.

I stopped at a gas station on my way to the hospital. After topping off the fuel tank, I went inside to grab some food for the road. I also picked up a bottle of water. If I took my medication without water, my throat would burn for hours.

Two white pills. One blue pill. I welcomed them into my body twice a day. My brain would kill itself without them. They held power over my future. If I elected not to ingest the tablets, I would be attending my own funeral instead of my dad's.

I got back into my silver Lexus RX300. When I started it, the belt squealed in protest of the looming 1,200-mile journey it had ahead. The small SUV was almost old enough to drink. Whenever my inner materialist noticed the peeling of the clear coat or the missing trim, I countered with "Yes, this car is old. The seats may be worn and starting to tear, but they are leather. The Mark Levinson stereo would still get any audiophile's ears to perk up. It's technically a luxury brand."

I left the gas station, the car silenced as the belt found its way back into place. The silver Lexus was telling me I had enough to worry about, and I had its support. With my junk food in hand and stereo cued to blare sad songs, I started back out on I-80 toward Utah. I went through Donner Pass, Truckee, and Reno for the first time since I got married.

Having been an only child my entire life, thirty-six months of companionship with my wife had taught me a lot. I was still adjusting. Having come from a family of ten, my better half didn't always understand some of my personality traits. Or the concept of being alone with one's thoughts.

My yearning for solace would be the sword with which I would either conquer life or fall on. Isolation was a survival technique. When in stressful environments, I coped well. When I knew I needed to go to my happy place and switch over my emotions to the backup generators inside my head, apathy was the way I survived.

Kimmy and I decided that it would be best for me to drive out alone. Then Kimmy would fly later with Elizabeth if she needed to help me with funeral arrangements. That way, we would save on airfare.

I gained some extremely rare time to meditate and process my own thoughts. At Donner Pass, reality set in for me. The dissension between my father and me had been escalating for the last several years. I wasn't sure of our current standing; now I may never know. All I could think about was a time in the not-so-distant past. A time when my father was already dead to me.

Chapter 4

Holding On with a Finger

2012

My worst fear came true. I had leaped to the other side of a gorge. I burned all the bridges leading back to my mother.

After my father left for Oregon, communication dwindled. We carried on corresponding for a short time, but it wasn't powerful enough to sustain a long-distance connection. Once my father realized the circumstances he put me in, he found that the easiest solution for him was to burn me like all the bridges he forced me to light ablaze when I left my mother for him. Though my father was content with his life choices and where they were leading him, I was stranded. In following my father, I'd unwittingly destroyed most of my relationships.

I had gambled on the fact that my father was the most promising route to survival. He wasn't. When people are young, they don't understand the concept of luck. There may be a winning streak for a little while. But sooner or later, the house always wins.

I had two years to navigate out of my childhood casino. I had no chips left. My luck had run out. I could also see security in the distance, seeking to remove me by force.

After spending eight months with my father, it was clear that I had a lot of work to do with the relationship between me and my mother.

I didn't know what to do. Dad had abandoned me. Just before he left, I learned that he'd been orchestrating all the motivation for me to abandon my mother in the first place. I was left to rebuild what was torn down.

2018
July 22, Sunday, 2:00 a.m.

I arrived at the hospital in the middle of the night. The building was locked. I had just driven six hundred miles to see my father, and now I couldn't even find a security guard. The campus was dark, and I felt disoriented. At one time, I had stayed in this hospital for my neurological health. All the muscle memory was gone. I had no clue what to do.

When I saw an ambulance pull up to the emergency entrance, I came apart. Tears welled up in my eyes. I became a lost child. I was alone. I was scared. I didn't know where my father was. My grasp of distance started to distort as the universe increased in size. For the first time, a new reality was mine to own. My father and I were finished. We had had our last exchange, our last communication. Our last phone call. Whatever our relationship was at the time, it would be forever. There was no future to it. Nor was there a present. My father and I were in the past. Or at least we would be shortly.

As the EMTs prepared the ambulance for the next call, I approached the emergency entrance of the hospital. It appeared to be the only part of the hospital that had any activity. I must have shown visible signs of distress because an EMT approached me.

"Are you okay?" he asked.

"No. My father is somewhere in this hospital. I don't know his room number. All the doors I tried are locked. I got lost in a stairwell. And if I don't find him soon, I will be the hospital's next patient."

"Do you know why he is here?"

"He is in the ICU. I think he is in a coma."

"Well, let's get you to the front desk to find his room number and then we will get you to the right place."

Jason, the EMT took me to the main lobby of the hospital. I gave the receptionist my father's name. I was directed to go to the neuro unit. My father was in the ICU there. A doctor would be with me shortly to go over the specifics of my father's case.

As I walked down the hallway to the elevator, I recalled the exact path that I would take to the neuro unit at Harborview Medical Center in Seattle. My father was not there for my brain surgery. It seemed only fitting that I missed his.

Chapter 5

A Little Walk

2013

November. I'd fallen down the stairs again. I didn't mind. This time nobody was home. Breaking a toe was a very mild boo-boo compared to the other epilepsy-related injuries I had inflicted on myself. This time I didn't end up facefirst in a discarded microwavable meal. My septum was already deviated six months prior when I fell into a wall. I didn't crack any more ribs. I was completely grateful that the episode ended with only a broken toe. I limped to my bedroom a happy camper.

As I was finishing up my splint job fashioned out of gray duct tape, I heard a telephone phone ring upstairs. It was Carla's. She had come home while I was passed out. I could tell from how she was talking who was on the other end of the line. Aunt Sharon had unexpectedly come to town. She only had a short while to visit and was on her way to Carla's house.

My head was pounding. Grand mal seizures were the latest development in my epilepsy. I would be out of commission for a day or more when I experienced one. A piercing headache, extreme fatigue, and nausea for forty-eight hours were the hallmark effects. As much as I wanted to visit with Aunt Sharon, I had to excuse myself. I went down to my room and crashed on my bed. When I woke up, I looked at the clock. I'd only been asleep for forty-five minutes.

My nausea had subsided. Apparently, a day had passed from the time I went down to my room. I was out of water in my mini fridge. I had to go back upstairs to restock. When I left my room, my mother was still in the living room. She looked at me and started crying. Carla, having gone an entire day without seeing me, was able to put two and two together to know that I had a seizure the previous day.

My grandmother walked down the hallway, reached out to me, and took me into an embrace which contained very confusing emotions. I couldn't translate what she was feeling or trying to communicate. Maybe Grandma was trying to hold those emotions back. After a while, she broke out of her hug and exhaled resiliently. I sat down on a chair next to my mother.

My mother couldn't maintain eye contact with me and keep control of her tear ducts at the same time. I was starting to become confused. They both knew my diagnosis. They were both at the last appointment with my neurologist.

We were all a bit emotional, but that had been two months ago. We knew what was going to happen. I wanted to live in the present. The future was too short to waste; the past was too complicated to reflect upon.

I could dissect my screwed-up life from beyond the grave. If I was right and there was an afterlife, I didn't need to worry about what might or might not happen. If the atheists were right, the whole damn thing was pointless anyway. I knew I was going to die. My father didn't care enough to be involved. My paternal grandparents would soon forget that I even existed.

I had mourned my own death. However, I knew that was not the case with Carla and Stacey. They would miss me. And for the remaining months I had on earth, my job was to prepare them for a picture which didn't include me.

Grandma pulled her cell phone out of her pocket. As I sat down, she dialed a number. The other end of the line opened. Carla, still holding back emotions, said, "He's awake."

"I will be there in ten minutes."

I thought I recognized the voice on the phone, but I couldn't be sure. Ten minutes later, two knocks on the door sounded. Carla opened the door.

Aunt Sharon stood in the doorway. "Oh, it's good to see you are awake Kameron. Do you feel like going for a walk?"

2018
July 22, Sunday, 2:20 a.m.

I reached the ICU. I gave the nurse at the front desk the room number that was written on my hand. She pointed. Dad's room was at the end of the hallway. The hallway was dim. Somehow, there was enough light to make out the lines on the floor. The floor was void of sound. Only voices that were not human could be heard. The voices belonged to medical equipment that supported and monitored the vital signs of their human patient counterparts. The noise was deafening, defined, and understandable.

I saw the room that my father was in. The echo of his machines was small at a distance. I started for his room. In other rooms, I saw monitors and support machines.

Soldiers stood on caster wheels. With rigid metal spines, they held a determined countenance that could be instantly trusted. They all were posted next to their assigned patients.

The man-made military was built to support and protect life. The machines never wavered, tirelessly pushing and pulling the breath out of their assignments. Pumping blood. Continuously reporting status and condition. A war between life and death ensued on the floor of the ICU. Though I was walking onto the battlefield, these machines were on the frontlines. However, they could only do so much. The life support machines were serving bodies not dissimilar from themselves. They both completed the same basic functions. One created by nature, one created by man. It was a pity that a man-made machine could not host a soul.

I came to my father's room. I saw the team that had kept him alive for the last twelve hours. I thanked them. They beeped in reassurance that they were dedicated to my father's survival. I saw my father in a white Hill-Rom hospital bed. His gown was down to his shoulders to make room for the brace around his neck. Various leads adhered to his chest. A nasogastric tube inserted through his right nostril was his only means of nutrition. A breathing tube connected his lungs to a BiPAP machine which was breathing for him.

A lead went to his head monitoring neuroactivity. I noticed his head was shaved back. He had a surgical incision. I thought it would be fun to compare scars after he got out; it was then that I remembered that we likely would never have that chance.

Dad's bed was at an incline. His feet extended beyond the edge of the bed, clothed in compression socks. His skin looked different. The man lying in the bed looked more like a wax figure of my father. I studied the man in the bed further. He became more realistic with time. More details crept through the shocking imagery. I was slowly but surely convinced that the comatose patient in the hospital bed was indeed my father.

I started talking. In all the movies, people in comas could supposedly hear what was going on around them. I figured I might as well let him know I was there.

"Dammit, Dad. What did you get yourself into this time?"

Unfortunately, I didn't get much of a response.

Mike Burton still hadn't shown up. We were alone in the hospital room together. It was like being on a desert island. It wasn't the first time I had been in the peculiar solace of an ICU. I felt a bit of comfort in the familiarity. As I held my dad's hand, I noticed some bruising above his IV, which was in his right arm. It was probably the result of an inexperienced nurse missing the vein. Then I saw another bruise on the back of his arm. It was as if the nurse had grabbed his wrist. My vision panned out to see his whole body in an overview.

Underneath the lead on his chest, a third bruise peaked out above the top of Dad's gown. I recalled the doctor's briefing, which included an injury to several of my father's ribs. I left his bed for the door. I checked the hallway. Not a single person in sight. I knew what was underneath the gown before I got back to the bed. I lifted the blanket up slowly. The bruising confirmed my suspicions. The ribs in question were indeed on the right side of my father's body.

My father and I had one mutual connection who had a history of aggressive behavior and physical violence. This person was nowhere to be found, despite his partner being at death's door. He had declined my recent calls and gone into radio silence. He also had a tendency to provide information only after making sure he wasn't putting himself at risk by doing so.

Mike was also left-handed.

Chapter 6

Walking into the Unknown

2013

"Yeah. Sure, where do you want to walk to?" I was a little confused by Aunt Sharon's proposal. Why would Sharon want to walk with me? Whenever she was in Utah, Sharon always spent her time either with her own family or Carla. Her time was very valuable and structured. It had to be. Uncle Tyler and Aunt Sharon were the most successful people I knew. Their lives ran like Swiss watches. Everything was scheduled, accounted for, and timed down to the minute. "Taking a walk" with me seemed a little out of character for Sharon. She must've thought it was worth doing, so I followed Sharon out the door. I looked back at Mom and Carla. They weren't coming. This was definitely weird.

We started walking when Sharon candidly asked, "Kameron, what do you want out of life?"

I replied, "I think that is kind of a moot point. A dead end, if you'll forgive the pun."

"Carla filled me in. She told me that your epilepsy is getting much worse. How are you dealing with that?"

"I think it's about par for the course. I knew the end would come eventually. In my case, I got a fast pass."

"So what are you going to do about it, Kameron?"

"I don't really have much to do. The only thing that sucks is medical insurance, which is hard enough to deal with when you have a preexisting condition. Try getting a life insurance policy. I don't know how that is going to work. Really the hardest thing to deal with is making sure that Carla and Stacey are all right with it. I'm pretty lucky actually. My dad doesn't know, and my dad's parents already said goodbye to me. So emotionally, I'm pretty set. I just need to run out the clock physically. I wish I were younger though. The whole Make-A-Wish thing looks cool. But the young kids with shaved heads are more enticing to supporters."

"Uncle Tyler and I think that there's another way."

"I know, I have looked into that with my neurologist. I've been on every medicine in the pharmacy, but it's still getting worse. They don't want to operate or do exploratory work. It's kinda final."

"We know that you have been struggling with this for quite a while, and Tyler and I want to help. Now, we can't promise anything, but we have done our own research. There are three top-rated neurology centers in the United States. One is in Boston. One is in San Francisco. The other center is at the University of Washington. It's a thirty-minute drive from where Uncle Tyler and I live. It is your choice. But if you would like, we would move you up to Washington to live with us. We can explore what options you truly have with a neurology team that is willing and able to approach this thing from all angles."

"What about Carla and Stacey? They are trying to take care of Joe. If I leave those two alone, there will be a murder. Do they know about this idea?"

"Kameron, you have spent your entire life worrying about your mom. The truth is, right now, if you don't spend a little time worrying about yourself, you won't be around to worry about anyone. What do you say? Would you like to come with us and give this a shot?"

We walked back to the house. My mother looked at me, desperate for an answer as if she already knew what was going on. We all sat in the living room together. Sharon looked at me and put the ball in my court. My mother's eyes begged me not to go. But her voice uttered a statement saying that it was for the best. Carla was overjoyed that I might actually have a shot at gaining back my life. However, even though her grandson may not have a pending death sentence anymore, she knew that her life sentence was with her daughter living in her basement. Now they would be alone without a pleasant son as a mediator and buffer.

Sharon handed me the envelope. Inside was a boarding pass for a flight to Seattle scheduled for January. In forty days, I would be in another state. Seeking a possibility of a second and third act to my life.

2018
July 22, Sunday, 3:50 a.m.

I left the ICU. I piloted my car to the only landing strip that had remained dependable my entire life. I had one person left in Utah that had remained steady. One person who I could invest a modicum of trust. An hour's drive brought me to my destination at 4:00 a.m. Someone who opens their door to you at four in the morning is either an extremely loyal or an extremely crazy person. Carla was both. The house was substantially bigger than it was five years ago. After Joe died, his bedroom became an office for Carla, and the room that used to be the office became a guest room. The kitchen table was completely empty. The basement in which I had resided in during the last few years of my childhood had been completely flushed. My mother's old room used to be hoarded out. Now it was empty. The carpet had been taken up and thrown out. The storage area underneath the living room once contained furniture dating back to the 1930s. Now it was void of any such furnishings. Nothing decorated the walls. Only the unfinished concrete of the foundation reflected back the dim light of the single incandescent lightbulb. The area in the basement located under the kitchen was where the washer and dryer were placed. They had not been used since I had lived there. Carla's body no longer permitted her to access the basement. All the Christmas decorations that used to be in the basement had vanished.

After forty-five years, my grandmother had purged her holiday decorations and only kept the most precious heirlooms. They now resided with her on the main floor. My room in the basement was all but empty. The only things remaining in the makeshift bedroom were a desk, an oak captain's bed, and a bare mattress sitting upon it that was purchased during the Clinton administration.

This basement had once been my home, or a place that one would list as their home. The address associated with the property was the most stable thing in my life. With the lowest level of my grandmother's house being stripped of all its contents, I was sure a gunshot down there would be much too loud to go undetected, like the old days.

Chapter 7

Trigger-Happy

2005

My mother and father never knew how good I was with a handgun. At nine years old, my shot grouping at ten yards was tighter than the tension in their marriage. More than a decade would pass before I could qualify for a Concealed Weapons Permit. My age didn't stop my grandfather from giving me an early education.

Joe was a gun enthusiast; he had turned to firearm sales and repair after his back injury forced him to quit auto body. I would come into the house and see a gun in one hundred pieces on the kitchen table. A walk out of the kitchen and the pistol would be magically reassembled. My mother liked guns but didn't necessarily like them around me. If I was in the area and there was a trace of a gun anywhere but my grandfather's bedroom, the reprimand he received was louder than the shot of the gun in question.

Gun control, in my grandfather's mind, was a pipe dream to anyone who thought it was even possible in the first place. When Grandma and my mom were away, our world was the Wild West. And Joe was the sheriff.

For as long as he had a car, every time I was with him was an opportunity to go Drag Mainstreet. It was our code for doing covert grandpa stuff that we didn't tell Mom or Grandma about. Twice a week, we would go get a Pepsi and go to the shooting range with whatever pistol he was working on (and a couple bricks of ammo).

It's harder to drag main without a car. When Grandma and the kids took his keys away, he had three things left. Television. Guns. And a loyal grandson. At ten years old, I knew how to shoot a gun in a basement without anyone hearing. I also knew that it was all my grandfather had left.

Stripping my grandfather of his freedom was the most painful thing I had seen up to that point in my life. Every passing day that Joe was held prisoner in his home, I saw him get more and more depressed. If he didn't get rid of those boxes of ammo somehow, I knew that there would be a day where I would be dropped off at his house to find that a round had gone through his head.

I walked in the door. He had been working at the kitchen table. The grip from his left hand on the small silver pistol was at half-mast. As he limply held the .380 Makarov PA-63, the gun had a presence in the room. As though the small, but potentially damning pistol was waiting faithfully for a command from its master. I feared the firearm may have already carried one such directive out.

I knew that they had been alone in the house together for the entire day. There was nobody to prevent the pistol from following orders from its owner, no matter how severe the consequence. The back of his head was facing the door. He was so still that I couldn't see if he was breathing. A blank stare from his eyes pointed at the television but failed to connect to it.

Today of all days, my mother decided to drop me on the sidewalk instead of leading me inside. Terrified, I backed out of the room. Out of habit I went for the phone in the office. The black corded phone that had been plugged into the wall for over twenty years had just been replaced with a cordless system. As fate would have it, the handset was not in the charger. Still not having backup on the way. I crept back into the kitchen. When I was close enough to see his face, I saw that his eyes had closed. Perfectly silent. Perfectly still.

I saw the cordless phone on the table. As I reached for the phone to place a call to 911, my other hand brushed against the side of his arm. Life left me as quickly as it went into him. With a loud snort, he startled awake from slumber. He was truly puzzled why I was there. We both found our equilibrium once we realized that his hearing aids were turned off. As he fiddled with the microscopic controls on his hearing device, he looked at me and uttered a simple statement, "Go down to the range, I'll grab some bricks of ammo from my room."

We couldn't go to the gun range anymore because it was farther than walking distance would permit. Grandpa decided to improvise. In the weeks before, we constructed a "range" of sorts for shooting in the basement. Grandma and Grandpa's basement was unfinished. Despite having the house provided to them after Joe's back injury by his brother, they never were able to build out the lower level. It was a straight shot from the basement door to the far wall of the foundation. just far enough to pass for a makeshift lane to shoot down. We would each go through one full clip. Shooting a handgun recreationally in his basement wasn't what relieved him of his Second Amendment right.

In some people's opinion, selling firearms at wholesale prices isn't an activity for a ten-year-old to be involved with. It also probably didn't help that my grandfather's clientele consisted of gang members, drug dealers, and other poor souls who couldn't afford or qualify for a firearm through traditional channels.

Carla never came home from work early. That day was a rare day. Joe had just finished a deal in the nick of time. The loyal client had just pulled away in his lowered and tinted black Mercedes 560SE. Carla's tires rested on the asphalt, which, moments ago, was occupied by a car that belonged to a Hispanic man who wore black. His button-down shirt, black. His pants, black. His leather watchband which matched his shoes, black. And his soul, a complimentary shade which would only get darker as his career progressed. My grandfather was confronted as soon as Carla walked in the door.

"Who was that?" she asked.

He replied, "A guy looking for help with a gun."

"*No. More,*" she gravely uttered.

Joe responded with a simple, "Okay."

The weekend passed. The following Tuesday, I was at Joe's place. The Mercedes presented itself in the driveway. I saw the man get out of his car and walk up to the door. Again, in black attire, he requested entrance into the dwelling by offering two concise knocks.

Grandpa and I looked at each other. He used his eyes to tell me that I need not mention this to Grandma. Uneasy, he approached the door. As Grandpa greeted the man with enthusiasm, the man looked over at me and removed his black Oakley sunglasses. Grandpa went to his room to retrieve his case that contained inventory for sale.

Grandpa came back to the room. As the man stood up from his chair, I noticed the shoulder holster peek out from his suit. A clip from an in-waistband holster rested on his belt. Joe notified the man that this would be the last deal between them due to Joe closing his operation.

After adding a black Glock 19 to his repertoire, the man gained another black accessory to his collection. An expression on his face that was darker than deep space. After a moment, The Man let out a very disturbing half smile. His gaze shifted to me.

"Are you sure you want to do that, Joe? We have been a very frequent customer of yours. Is it the money? Is it the…motivation?"

Grandpa responded nonverbally before he spoke. Grandpa took the Sig Sauer P220, which was chambered.

He pulled the hammer back and replied with a damning "Yep. It's just quitting time."

The man took the Glock 19 and left the cash on the table. This time the tinted Mercedes left in plenty of time for Grandpa and me to get our story straight.

I knew why Grandpa had chosen the gun he had used to make his point. A Glock 19 is extremely accurate at long distance. A Sig P220 will send one person to two circles of hell with a lone .45-caliber round. Things one learns from a grandfather that is a gunsmith.

Friday. Two days passed since the final business deal. When I saw Grandpa Joe, his hands were bruised, and his face was severely cut. On Thursday he had apparently "tripped down the last few stairs into the basement and hit the concrete." I never saw the black Mercedes or the man who drove it again.

2018
July 22, Sunday, 9:00 a.m.

The alarm on my iPhone ended my inadequate sleep. I was not only tired; I was also confused. The default xylophone tune erupted from the telephone. Every morning it told me that my wife was up already, browsing social media. Waiting for the inevitable request from the next room to get up. The sound was a warning that if I wanted a shower, I had ten minutes before the day started.

That morning I rolled over and sprawled my arms across the bed. To my surprise, I was alone. Nobody was there. I looked up and saw the brass headboard that used to belong to my grandfather. I was in Utah. It wasn't a dream. My father was indeed in a hospital. I wanted nothing more than to wake up. I slid out of the bed and walked across the hallway to the bathroom. It had changed significantly since Joe had gone. The blue flower print linoleum from 1978 had been replaced with tile. A small granite remnant took the place of the white-and-blue Formica that I had grown up with. A stackable washer-dryer combo was a new addition as well. Not remembering the appliance was there, I walked right into it and stubbed my toe.

I looked into the mirror and searched for some sort of foothold to climb back up to reality with. I knew that it wasn't really reality that I wanted. What I truly desired was an escape. I wanted to be elsewhere. A foothold would save me. But ultimately, I wanted to just let go. I wished that I could break the mirror. I wanted to be on the other side of it. I wanted my vision to end at the walls of that room.

But unfortunately, I was on the human side of the mirror. I could see more than just my reflection. I saw my future. The future staring back at me didn't involve a person who had been my guardian for most of my life. As I gazed into the mirror, the reflection changed. I saw a man that no longer reported to his elders.

I drove to the hospital at ten in the morning. Lying there on the bed was my father, or what was left of him. he was alone. The nurse I saw earlier that morning was nearing the end of her shift. I asked her if my father had any visitors. She said I was the last person to come to his room. Mike hadn't come by. It was late in the morning and still no sign of the person who claimed to be the closest person to my father. I decided to wait in the room just in case Mike Burton showed up.

I called my grandparents. They lived an hour away from the hospital. They were driving to Salt Lake City. While I prepared for seeing them again, I occupied myself with other matters. With three hours of precious sleep under my belt, I couldn't help but lie back in the chair next to Dad's bed. The BiPAP machine connected to my father sang me to sleep.

Chapter 8

A Shocking Turn of Events

2012

That weekend was a long weekend. Longer for Mike Burton. Time is harder to pass on vacation when one is in handcuffs. The universe handed me another chance to get rid of Mike Burton. My conscience told me to hand it back and spit in the universe's face. They say that when someone jumps to their death, it's not the impact that kills them; it's the terror. The emotion induces a panic that causes a cardiac event in the jumper. They aren't even conscious when they hit the ground.

Part of me wanted him to feel it. The concrete smashing against his joints. His head. Gravity using the pavement to redefine his current state. A redefinition just as abrupt as when the universe used Mike Burton to change me when he entered my life. But I had raised myself better. I was almost seventeen years old. I knew that I'd regret it if I let him take a shortcut to the lobby from the top floor. So I called the cops on Michael Burton. Again.

Friday. It was going to be a three-day weekend. We were going to spend the weekend at a high-end hotel. We were going to chill out and celebrate Mike Burton getting visitation rights back from his ex-wife. We were going to have a nice evening with an alcohol-free dinner. We were going to have a carefree weekend that wouldn't have a lasting impact on the future. We were going to stay status quo. What we became was something else entirely.

I got home from school. Mike was waiting. Bags were packed, loaded into the car. We got into Mike's Audi and headed out for Salt Lake City. the Embassy Suites were waiting for us. But first, dinner at P. F. Chang's. Chang's, from my experience, appeared to be the homosexual equivalent to Hooters. My dad and Mike daintily built their lettuce wraps as they drooled over the young twentysomethings. Dressed in fitted black dress shirts, the waiters who tended the tables in the restaurant were definitely attractive. My father and his partner seemed to forget that they were both in a supposedly committed relationship. I sat and watched as they drooled over the staff. The most painful part to witness was the fact that they seemed to think of themselves as eligible bachelors and in the same league as the blond, built, and tattooed twenty-four-year-old waiter named Derek.

It was when the waiter made a pity pass at my father that things went south. The waiter noticed blaring signals from the two men in their forties and felt a bit charitable. Much in the way that a movie star would compliment a Make-A-Wish kid, Derek complimented my dad's scarf and admired how it matched his eyes. Mike Burton did not receive such a compliment. When my father blushed and reacted like a schoolgirl, Mike's eyes burned with territorial anger.

It wasn't clear at the time whether Mike was threatened more by a lack of attention from the waiter or from my father. The one certainty was that the mood for the night was changing. The absence of alcohol for the weekend was no longer a hope. The presence of alcohol dissolved any predictability.

What worried me the most was that we were not at home. This was going to be an away game. I lost my home-court advantage. That advantage was precious to me. I looked down and found a small comfort when I saw my feet were sporting very appropriate attire for the unknown—running shoes.

Mike immediately requested a bottle of white wine. Derek showed up moments later with said bottle in hand. When the waiter began to pour, Mike intervened with a sharp "We've got it, thanks!" Derek immediately received the message and disappeared. Sauvignon

Blanc vanished almost as quickly from Mike's glass. A serious and mildly uncertain expression appeared on Dad's face. I knew that they had a mutual commitment to stop drinking. It had been five days since either one of them had a drink. We finished dinner, with a single glass of wine going to my father, likely medicinal. I could see in my father's eyes that he knew he would have to calm his nerves for the rest of the weekend. The rest of the bottle had been thoroughly depleted by Mike Burton.

We got in the car. Dad was behind the wheel. Before he straightened the wheels after pulling the Audi out of the space in the parking garage, Mike adamantly suggested a detour to the liquor store to stock up for the weekend. He had fallen asleep in the passenger seat by the time we got to the street level of the garage. Before Dad inserted the ticket into the machine that would allow us to exit, I made a plea.

I said, "Mike is out, let's just go to the hotel."

"You know what will happen when he wakes up and realizes that we didn't go," Dad replied.

"And you know what will happen if he drinks all weekend. I thought you two were getting back on the wagon!"

"Sometimes a wheel breaks, Kameron."

"Then go fix it, Dad."

"I will after the weekend. I just want to get through this without drama."

Dad put the ticket in, and the arm raised, giving us the freedom to get on the road. Neither one of us wanted it. My father knew damn well that there would be drama, regardless of what direction he drove the car.

"Pick your poison, Dad."

"I'm sorry, Kam, we are going to just have to deal with this."

"Yep, I guess we are."

My father, with a sharp left turn, pointed Mike's Audi toward the liquor store. It wasn't the first time I had followed him into hell. I knew what I had signed up for when I chose my father. For the first time, my pace was getting harder to maintain. My view of the finish line was getting darker. My ankles ached. My heart ached too. I saw the time I had lived with them as pavement. I could use it as a surface to run across. I could also trip and fall on it. I couldn't look down. I didn't want to visualize my face scraping the asphalt. I didn't want to feel the burns on my arms from bracing against the ground. My only choice was to keep sprinting forward. The oxygen would come. The energy would come. The will would come. The future would come.

Parked at the liquor store, Mike Burton woke up. He reached for his cell phone. My father was inside, picking out supplies for the weekend. Mike dialed Dad. Dad instantly answered. Mike wanted two bottles of Skyy, a bottle of Tito's, and a bottle of Smirnoff. Dad acquiesced and came out a little while later with paper bags. Their contents were masked by the brown color of the bags. I felt like I had a connection to the brown paper bags. We both had a job to do that night. Their job was to hide a cause. My job was to hide an effect. At that moment, neither one of us knew if we would be able to do our job effectively.

Dad got back into the car. Mike examined the haul. He seemed pleased. We drove to the hotel. Dad checked in. When we got up to the hotel room, Mike waited impatiently for a drink. Dad emptied a suitcase and went down to the car to smuggle the booze in. I needed to get my bearings. I approached the door to leave.

Mike Burton asked, "Where do you think you are going?"

I picked up the cooler and said, "I'm going to get ice. You want anything?"

"Get some peanuts," he grumbled.

I got out of the room and found myself in the hallway. There were four levels. We were on the third. I took my cell phone out and took a picture of the fire exit diagram. Two elevators, two stairwells. One stairwell connected to the adjacent parking structure. I still didn't know what would or wouldn't happen, but I knew the layout. I knew my exit strategy. I had a flight plan. I came back with ice and peanuts. Dad was back. So was the booze. The TV was on. The conversation was louder.

Mike Burton was well into a bottle of Tito's vodka. Fun Drunk Mike was only with us for a short time. He was then replaced with Introspective Drunk Mike. I was always most wary of Introspective

Drunk Mike. The most dangerous thoughts always came to him then. Almost immediately after, Angry Drunk Mike came out to play. He wasn't too happy about Derek from P. F. Chang's. The evening was filled with on and off one-sided bickering from Mike about the hot twentysomething who had the nerve to come onto my father. As minutes turned into hours, the drinking progressed. Soon the two bottles of Skyy were down to a half. And only a few shots worth of Tito's remained in the bottle.

My father had called it a night at about eleven thirty. Mike Burton stayed up with the vodka well into the wee hours of the morning. He had taken off his shirt and was missing his pants. Vodka in large amounts had a way of turning Mike Burton into a minimalist. I woke up to the sound of crying and yelling. Dad was awake again.

Mike sobbed about neglect from my father and questioned the worth of his own life. Near the point of alcohol poisoning, Mike was treading on the brink of disaster. My father tried to approach him, but Mike would not have it. The noise was building. I convinced my father to stay sitting on the bed while I talked to Mike in the bathroom. Mike Burton was sitting on the edge of the bathtub with the bottle of Skyy. He would definitely describe it as half-empty. I regarded it as half-full. I knew that this was not bottom. Bottom was at the end of that bottle. The situation could get a lot worse than it was at that present time. The remaining alcohol was the agent to take us there.

I stood in the hallway. I placed myself in the mind of a suicidal man. In a bathroom. I counted fourteen ways that Mike Burton could end it. I also knew that getting too close to him was one way to get myself killed.

Part of me wanted to let the chips fall. To let him end it. To give him what he wanted. I turned my head from the suicidal mess in the hotel bathroom and looked at another man sitting on the king-size bed in the fetal position, crying. Unfortunately for me, If I gave in and let Mike Burton take his own life, my father wouldn't survive. I would likely have to clean up two deaths.

I looked back at Mike. I approached the door; he slammed it in my face. He told me not to come in. If I wasn't going in, I needed him to come out. After he slammed the door, security knocked on the door of the hotel suite. Mike cracked the bathroom door open. He whispered to me, "If you let them in, I'll do it right now."

"Okay. I'll get rid of them." I opened the door to the suite.

Security told me that there had been multiple noise complaints.

Dad got up from the bed and said that there wasn't anything to worry about. He told them that we were fine, I corroborated. The guards seemed to buy it. I knew I had to get Mike Burton out of the bathroom. Dad went back to the bathroom door and pleaded with Mike to come out. He told Mike that he was sorry about the waiter and it would not happen again. He was sorry for everything.

I left the suite, leaving the door cracked. Security was still in the hallway. I asked them if they would hang around a little bit. They gave me a nonverbal confirmation that they would. I went back to the hotel room.

Mike was barely conscious in the bathroom. I opened the bathroom door and entered. He was sitting in the bathtub in his underwear. It was apparent that he didn't value life. Mike didn't value my father or me. He didn't care about his children. At that moment, Mike Burton was just one selfish, lost soul who had way too many people around him that valued his life more than he did.

The only thing he valued in the world was in his hand. A bottle fashioned out of glass. The only logical approach was to remove it from him. I ripped the Skyy out of his left hand. He didn't like that. Mike stumbled out of the bathroom and yelled at me. Security took that as a cue and made their grand entry. Mike evaded them and went for the front door. He ran through the main concourse of the hotel, drunk and wearing nothing but avocado-colored Banana Republic briefs. I recalled the layout of the floor. I knew what he was looking for. My only edge was that he didn't know where to find it. I got the attention of the security guards.

"He is going to jump, parking garage! Roof!"

Mike saw the sign indicating stairs were around the corner and rushed for them. The guards followed. He got up to the roof. As he looked down at what seemed to be his only option, he started crying. The guards stalled him. I didn't know what to say to him. Dad soon arrived and wasn't much help either. Mike was only aggravated. He was adamant that if we tried to talk him down, he would just jump. Mike got what he wanted, kind of. Mike Burton did drop to the ground that night. Two leads connected to a high voltage battery sprang from the guard's Taser gun. One lead went into his lower back. The other lead implanted firmly into his left upper thigh. With the sound of several clicks, he shook and collapsed. Mike spent the rest of the weekend in jail on a three-day psychiatric hold.

I kept my running shoes. But I was out of steam. I didn't know where the finish line was anymore. I lay on the pavement that was my life, road rash on my arms, scrapes, and bruises everywhere on my body. My soul was dehydrated. My will was hemorrhaging blood. I looked up into the sky and just closed my eyes. Something would come. It would save me, build me, or kill me. But come, it would. The only thing I had left in the world was the uncomfortable truth that the marathon would never stop. Even though I hated that truth, it would never betray me or lie to me.

When dad and I got home, I went to my bedroom after he passed out from the stress of the night before. I opened the bottom drawer of my dresser. Hidden underneath a leather jacket, my folded-up American Tourister go-bag was about to be recommissioned.

2018
July 22, Sunday, 11:00 a.m.

I woke to the sound of my grandfather talking to my grandmother about me. They were both crying. Their only son was in a coma. Lifeless but alive in a hospital bed.

"How long has Kameron been here?"

"Should we wake him?"

"Did he drive here through the night?"

I thought the best option was to give them a moment alone with Dad.

After all, this was an experience that isn't typical on the standard agenda of life. Children bury parents. That is the natural order of life.

When reversed, that process results in a paralyzing and concentrated form of devastation.

His father was broken. His mother was crushed. Like a broken Japanese vase, they would no longer exist as they once had. Michael's absence broke them into shards of broken porcelain. The burden would fall upon them to find mortar to form themselves into something beautiful once again. Using what pieces remained, they were about to come to an unexpected point in their lives. A point that would force them to stay broken or transform into something new. Regardless of which path they chose, the absence of their son would change the shape in which they existed.

Phyllis walked up to her son. The sight of him pushed against her, but she did arrive at his hand. She took Dad's hand in hers. As she tried to comprehend, the burden of her emotions finally cracked the yoke she was carrying upon her shoulders. Everything spilled. Tears rushed down her cheeks and down her neck. Her forehead burned and turned red. Charles came to her side to offer comfort and took Michael's other hand. In the two decades that I had known my grandfather, I hadn't ever witnessed him cry tears of sadness. I had assumed he followed the same record for the previous forty years of his life as well. This was different. His eyes watered. He didn't brush the salty tears from his face as they were foreign to him.

Phyllis sought breath in the hallway. She exited the hospital room and stood next to a group of chairs. Charles remained in the room. I decided it was time to wake up. I opened my eyes and rose from my chair. Grandpa noticed that I was awake and put a hand on my shoulder as I came to the foot of the bed.

"I'm so sorry, Kameron."

"Me too, Grandpa."

"How long have you been here?"

"I got in this morning at two."

"Do you have someplace up here? Are you staying at Carla's?"

"Yep, I am staying with Carla. I'm going to go check on Grandma."

"Okay." Charles remained at the feet of his only son.

I left the hospital room and found her in the hallway. Grandma was visibly not all right. I went and sat beside her. As soon as I drew in close enough to be at arm's length from her, she pulled me into an embrace which lasted quite a while. I knew she wished that she were holding her son. I couldn't be him. But I could be someone. So I was, for her, someone.

Neither one of us quite knew how to comprehend what was going on. Dad wasn't dead. But he very soon would be. She didn't know why. Charles didn't know why.

Until this was over, I had to be present. I had to be involved. If that was going to happen, my emotions would need to be controlled somehow. I knew I would be facing the entity that ultimately broke my father. If I was going to get through this, I needed help. I had to summon the part of me that had no soul. The partition of my conscience that had been dormant and damned for five years. The part of me that quietly dealt with problems. Nobody knew why we were here. I had far fewer questions than everyone else. What I knew about my father's life would only cause more pain. Charles came out of the room and joined us in the hallway.

Then Phyllis asked me, "Has Mike Burton been here?"

I replied with a simple, "Not yet."

Chapter 9

Up in Smoke

2012

I didn't make it through school without being offered a cigarette. It came from Mike Burton. I knew exactly what I would be signing up for if I started smoking. Genetically, I won the addictive personality lottery. I knew that if I ever touched nicotine, my brain would grasp it with an iron grip that would likely outlast lung cancer.

We were in the garage. Mike was smoking and drinking. The door was up. With a Wasatch white IPA beer in his left hand and a Marlboro Red in his right, he was dancing to the Pet Shop Boys at a volume which was low, but definitely audible to a passerby. He had gotten sloppy about keeping his presence at the house concealed. Dad stopped caring too. And I didn't possess the authority to enforce their own house rules.

Mike was numbing the pain of disappointment. I was a much-desired company to his misery. When he needed a boost to his confidence, Mike was the type to show off. As he continued to attempt to blow smoke rings, I took a seat in one of the three canvas lawn chairs that were used to furnish the garage. He was halfway into the six-pack of beer when he asked me if I'd ever smoked. I said no. He then motioned to his pack of cigarettes and said, "Go grab one."

It was the first time I had ever picked up a pack of cigarettes. I opened the top and pulled one out. I held the smoke in my hand and evaluated it. I marveled at how small it was, relative to the repercussions of smoking it. I put it in my mouth. The paper taste was odd when mixed with the smell of the tobacco.

I leaned forward as Mike Burton passed me his gray Bic lighter. I spun the flint wheel and flame poured out the end. The flame was steady. It bobbed up and down from the top of the lighter, searching for something to ignite.

I looked up from the cigarette and back at Mike. At $6.50 a pack, I was giving myself over to a $2,000 per year habit. I knew Mike Burton started smoking when he was my age. He had been smoking on and off for twenty-eight years. An unemployed forty-four-year-old drunk with a criminal record was sitting beside me. He lounged in a broken lawn chair. Beside him, was a leased Audi S4 that he couldn't afford.

Because of his life choices, Mike could only maintain a facade. Mike Burton only possessed the illusion of success. In reality, he had nothing. If his image were to ever be truly examined, everything about Mike Burton crumbled.

I moved the unlit cigarette back and forth with my tongue. I politely put the smoke back on the table and then made a promise to myself. In twenty-eight years, I would purchase an Audi S4 as a forty-fifth birthday present to myself with the $66,430 I kept away from Phillip Morris.

2018
July 22, Sunday, 12:00 p.m.

Still no sign of him. Mike Burton was missing, Dad was alive, but gone. The longer we waited in the hospital room, the harder it was to not think about time. Time was the elephant in the room. Nobody could ignore it. Time dominated us. Time held our minds captive. Time was a question. Time was an answer. Time was a commodity. How much time was left? What did we want more of than anything else? Time. There was nothing that we wouldn't trade for more of it.

Ultimately, we didn't have control over time. One person was calling the shots. Nobody knew of a directive from my father. There was no known will. We couldn't turn off the machines or keep them on. Law dictated that only the closest next of kin was able to make calls concerning what happened next. Dad's closest next of kin was still yet to be seen.

My father's sisters came into the room. I watched reality grab my aunts. It shoved them and kicked them while they were down. The sight of their only brother broke them. Katie and Michelle couldn't comprehend reality without their lifelong friend and confidant.

Katie cupped her hands to her mouth, trying to muffle her heart as it screamed from being pierced with unbelief. Tears rushed from her eyes. Rapids poured down her cheeks and washed her hands away. Katie's hands flailed as her arms searched for home. Her arms would never again be embraced by her brother, her protector.

Michelle saw him. The room instantly emptied. Only she and her brother remained. Struck with the absence of Michael, she searched for her brother. When he didn't respond to her touch, anger took over. Why would he not respond? For Michelle's entire life, Michael had never once ignored her. He had always been there for her. Why wasn't he responding now? Michelle was desperate for an embrace from her brother. So was Katie. They could only find comfort in each other now.

I watched the family come together for the first time without Michael. I was about to join when I saw a doctor stationed outside the room. He was waiting to come in, but after a career filled with these types of interaction, he knew the proper time and a place for logistics.

I stepped closer to the family locked in a single embrace. Before I reached them, I was mauled. I looked to identify who was attacking me, but my sense of smell beat my eyes to the punch.

For some reason, Mike Burton was totally convinced that Polo Red, Ralph Lauren for Men, completely erased all traces of the scent of alcohol from his body. In reality, Malibu coconut rum mixed with

Polo Red is reminiscent of rat urine. Add a little body odor and cigarette smoke, the scent would kill a rat.

He was wearing a yellow golf shirt made of stretch material that barely accommodated his figure. His designer blue jeans were worn out and had been on his body for more than three days. His nicotine-stained fingers ran through my hair and pulled my head into his chest. Miraculously, the aroma didn't knock me unconscious.

The chief neurologist walked in. He ushered us into a conference room. The door closed. The firm sound the door made as it closed gave me more information than the doctor would. I knew that in hospitals, good news is never broken behind closed doors.

As we looked at the brain scans projected onto the screen, all the details faded as the doctor proceeded to tell us that Michael's chance of waking up were zero. My father was brain-dead. My father was now a machine. Hooked to other machines. Pumping blood through veins and organs. Mike Burton fled the room.

The organ donation coordinator came in. I looked over at my grandmother. A mother was being approached by a woman who wanted her son's organs. Phyllis appeared to implode from the force the world was putting on her. She couldn't comprehend that her only son was now nothing more than a body. The body which represented her son was now being considered as nothing more than spare parts for other people.

I knew that in another life, Dad would have sacrificed as much as he could for other people. In the latter part of his life, he was searching for something that would redeem himself. We put it to a vote. Although the result was a unanimous yes, the choice ultimately was possessed by someone who was no longer present. We waited in the conference room for Mike Burton. Katie was about to boil over.

After about two minutes, Katie stood up from her chair.

"This is absolutely ridiculous! *We* are Michael's family! Mike showed up ten minutes ago. *We* have been here for hours! Mike Burton shouldn't be the person in charge here! He hasn't been present for any of this. If anything, it should be Kameron! We are blood!"

"We all agree, Kate," Phyllis said.

Mike entered the room. The coordinator updated Mike Burton. He was in favor of organ donation. Mike Burton asked if there would be an autopsy. When the donation coordinator said that there would be an autopsy conducted either way, blood drained from his face, and he replied, "I don't think Michael would want that. He also told me that he wanted to be cremated."

Chapter 10

Life in a Bag

2012

Nearly a year of shared custody made me mindful of my material possessions. The first month of living in two households was a tremendous adjustment. It took a toll on my sense of stability. What if I ran out of something? What if I left something important at the other house? What if I pack too much? What do I do with my laundry? How do I fit everything into one suitcase? How do I pack my life into a suitcase?

After a month of struggle, I understood that the bag was never going to get bigger. If I ever wanted to feel control again, I needed to accept that my life had to get smaller.

1 pillow
1 hygiene kit
8 shirts
8 pairs of underwear
3 pairs of pants
5 pairs of socks
1 cell phone + charger
1 laptop + charger
1 month's supply of medication

1 Casio F-91W watch
1 Dockers brown leather wallet

My life at the time required less than thirty-five things. With mindful packing they all fit into a small duffel bag. The bag was given to me by my father after the separation. The duffel bag was in very good shape despite having many miles on it. Dad had used it heavily for various things. The black American Tourister was used by my father for car auctions, auto shows, dealer expos, business trips, and of course, personal affairs. The bag accommodated my needs very well.

As things with Dad and Mike Burton deteriorated, I sat in my bedroom and listened to the war. Every once in a while, my thoughts and eyes would shift from the sounds of battle. I'd look over to my dresser. I seldom used the drawers, as I rotated between my mother's home and my father's.

Now, the drawers in the dresser at my father's apartment were filled. I was no longer living out of the bag. My life was tied down. I had normalcy. This was how regular people lived. My black duffel was stowed away, concealed underneath my winter clothes in the bottom drawer. I told myself that I'd never use the bag again.

I was raised not to steal. I was also raised not to drink. So the first time I stole money was from my father, and I did it while he was too wasted to notice. Dad and Mike were having a fun night of drinking, relaxing, and watching sports. My father never watched sports before Mike Burton came into the picture and I knew damn well he just did it because Mike Burton enjoyed them.

They ran out of mixers. With the absence of mixers, Mike Burton and my father transitioned to straight alcohol. I let them know we were running low while I still had a chance. After all, I wasn't just a bartender. I was a bartender who cared.

At seventeen, my father thought I was old enough to make mixed drinks, but I still couldn't drive because of my seizures. Dad jumped at the opportunity to call a timeout and take a break from basketball. We went to Macey's grocery store to get some Coke and juice. My dad was sober enough to drive but too inebriated to be in public. I offered to go in and grab the requested merchandise. Dad accepted my gesture. He handed me his debit card. That was my chance. He only used debit when he had a decent amount of money in the bank. I went in and picked up the usual—Cherry Coke, Simply Lemonade, Minute Maid, and cranberry juice. After I had what they needed, I ran to the front to do a little shopping for myself.

I searched where the gift cards were located. Sure enough, the prepaid cell phones were right next to the cards. I picked up the cheapest one and a sixty-minute card for $40. When I checked out, the terminal gave me the option of cashback. I had a problem maintaining my cool when the terminal approved $80, bringing my total to $150. The card went through. I walked out the door. Through a windshield covered in raindrops, I could see the outline of Dad sitting in the car. He had fallen asleep waiting for me. I put the bags in the trunk.

The $80 was the beginning of my emergency fund. I stashed the money in a second wallet to be hidden in my go-bag. I hid the phone in the trunk next to the spare tire.

When we returned home from the store, Mike Burton and Dad continued to drink and curse at the television. I retrieved my second cell phone and second wallet from the garage. My life could still fit in a duffel bag; a wallet filled with cash and a burner phone didn't add a lot of weight. I hid them in the bottom dresser drawer underneath my sweaters. If I had to leave, soon I'd be able to. The black American Tourister, once a symbol of uncertainty, now epitomized my best chance of obtaining a future—a future that I was in control of. I could grab onto my bag's leather handle bound by brass rivets. As long as my grip on the bag was solid, I could evacuate at a moment's notice.

I could go without fear. All I lacked was cash. I didn't find it that hard to figure out. Mike and Dad were drinking well into the early morning. They'd be sleeping until eleven. Mike Burton did not exactly watch his finances like a hawk. The next day, I started circling.

2018
July 22, Sunday, 12:30 p.m.

Cremation. It was such an odd word. Nothing about the word felt right. When I heard the word out loud, the only image I could put together was that of cake—maybe a beverage associated with coffee and sugar. Cremation was a white ice cream cake. I stared at Mike blankly as the tinnitus in my ears flared up. The ringing in my ears canceled out everything. The only thing in my brain was the thought, "Mike, my father doesn't want to be a cake."

My mind was slipping out of the room. The sound of Phyllis and Katie wailing caught my mind by the wrist and pulled it back in. Cremation was not what it sounded like. The definition of cremation was "to reduce a dead body to ashes by burning." A crematorium was not a factory where ice cream was produced. According to *Merriam-Webster*, it was "an establishment or structure in which the bodies of the dead are cremated." I saw the horror and fear in my grandparents' eyes. Their only son was soon going to die. And the person sitting across the table from them was adamant that the body be disposed of and burned as quickly as possible.

I looked down the table at Mike. I knew what he was. I knew who he was. I knew how he dealt with things. But he didn't know me. He was partially responsible for who I was. In the time that I had known Mike Burton, he had taught me how to shape my conscience. Before I met Mike Burton, I had a level of apathy in my soul, which allowed me to survive. My ability to turn into Mr. Hyde came after I knew Mike. Mike Burton was the master blacksmith who quenched the darkness inside me into hardened steel. Living with him gave me a unique insight to what went on between Mike and my father. I looked into Mike's eyes.

I searched through the tears of sadness. Behind them, I saw fear. Behind the fear, I found the man that I tried so hard to forget. I found the man that had a history of violence. The same man who dislocated my father's jaw with a DVD player. I saw a man who I once knocked out with a glass bottle in self-defense. He was a man who tried to assault me and had beaten my father several times. I found the devil. He also was an enthusiastic advocate for destroying the body of his partner. My father wasn't even dead yet. Mike Burton was absolute and eerily lucid about the arrangements.

When Mike Burton called me in the middle of the night earlier in the week, I knew he was going to tell me that my father was in the hospital. He had done so at least four times in the last two years. I reflected on the first time he alerted me in the middle of the night. It was due to a mugging. An LGBT hate crime. They also happened to be in Portland at the time. Then I thought, a hate-motivated attack on a gay couple would be likely in a conservative area. In the LGBT capital of the Pacific Northwest seemed a bit out of place. Falling off a barstool does not break three ribs and cause a coma.

Chapter 11

A Well-Warranted Vacation

2012

My envelope had nearly $400 in it. My bag contained everything I needed from Dad's apartment. If a time presented itself, I would be ready. We were headed to Oregon for the weekend. Mike's home in Bend was on the market, and he had gotten an offer. After a day of tourism in Portland, we went back to the hotel. Little did I know that this wasn't just any trip. The weekend was a showcase. For Mike Burton to get everything he wanted, he had to deal with the baggage first. That baggage was me.

I was already detached from my mother. Mike Burton stole my father away from her. Now Mike had to steal him away from me. Mike had a dilemma. If he couldn't get my father to abandon me, he had to win me over. Worst case scenario, Mike got a stepson.

I was a tripwire on the way to completing his plan of getting Michael to himself. If he crossed me, there was no telling what could happen. Would my dad leave him? How much exactly, could he get away with? Mike Burton tried to court me with cars and money.

In a mere two days, Mike convinced my father that Oregon was the answer to their problems. Moving to Oregon would clear away all of Dad's problems. He could leave the job he hated. He could stop associating with the people that turned against him. He would obtain even more distance from his parents, who, in Mike's view, were less than supportive of his lifestyle. Oregon would be a fresh start for my father. There was one hurdle that my father didn't quite know how to cross, me.

Mike Burton and my father were either unaware or careless of the fact that they were committing a crime. By taking me across state lines, Dad had committed parental kidnapping. The custody document stated that custody was divided equally between my mother and father. If Mom ever caught wind of the fact that I had gone to Oregon with Dad and Mike Burton, she could have sent my father to jail. I added one more block to my tower of secrets. It was heavy, unstable, and liable to fall to the ground. Something had to change.

Another weekend of drunken madness had passed by. Mike locked up the house and said goodbye to it. We set out on the road. Destined for Utah, I sat in the back seat. I looked past my father's hand intertwined with Mike Burton's on top of the center console.

A spiraled power cord was plugged into the cigarette lighter. The cable crept up the dashboard and connected to a radar detector mounted on the windshield. The last thing we needed was to be pulled over for speeding. Mike already had a warrant out for his arrest. And now he had an alleged kidnapper in the passenger seat. It was difficult to determine whether the two men were letting go of their problems or picking up more. It could also be argued either way whether they were about to lose everything they had or if they were about to obtain everything they ever wanted in life. The one certainty was that their grip was very faint.

Three loud beeps from the radar detector alerted Mike burton of a speed trap. He slowed and saw the Oregon state trooper waiting on the overpass. We all perked up and waited for a sign of pursuit. I looked through the rear window and saw the dark brown 2007 Crown Victoria shift into gear. The state trooper moved across the overpass and shot down the onramp. With one fluid merge, he was right behind us at eighty-eight miles per hour.

Mike's first reaction was that of surprise. Then fear set in. After fear, anger.

"*Shit.*"

"Honey, we are screwed! Why were you speeding?" Dad's voice sounded scared and furious.

"I *know*. I was keeping up with traffic!" Mike replied defensively.

"Why aren't you pulling over?" Dad appeared to be truly frightened.

"He hasn't turned on his lights yet," Mike replied hesitantly.

"Are you seriously thinking..." Dad had known Mike long enough to see options through Mike Burton's lens

"I can get in front of that truck and cut off at the exit." Mike was always too confident for his own good.

"*He has your plate, Mike! Pull over.*" Dad looked pissed.

"Yeah, and go back to jail? *Uh-huh*. We can get lost in a parking lot or something," Mike replied, adamant about evading another prison experience.

The Oregon state trooper turned on its lights. Mike shot past a white freightliner semitruck. With less than a car length's clearance, he managed to get us off the freeway. I watched as the state trooper continued in pursuit of the yellow Porsche 911, which was going well above one hundred miles per hour.

"Mike, he was on someone else. We're safe," I said. I was relieved we were alive. But the back of that car was the last place I wanted to be.

"Fuck! Your turn to drive, babe." Mike seemed to wash his hands of responsibility.

Mike parked at a Taco Bell. He got out of the running car and Dad took the wheel. Abundant with caution, Dad got back onto the freeway. From then on, we traveled at no faster than sixty-seven miles per hour.

I gazed through the windshield. The radar detector was silent. So was I. We both scrutinized the open road ahead of us. The radar detector and I were not so different. We both sought after the same things. A policeman, a symbol of order, a path to control, a portal to safety. I knew that I wouldn't be able to find any. The only practical options for me were on another road. My road was a forgotten road. It was an abandoned road. This road was paved with good intentions. But the bridge that connected to it was burned out of self-preservation. I didn't know how. But I was not going to be able to control my fate in Oregon. I would have to rebuild the bridge to my mother.

2018
July 22, Sunday, 12:45 p.m.

Mike was still sobbing. I drew in a breath and exhaled slowly. As everything became clear. I closed my eyes. My right thumb rubbed the scar tissue on my third finger. The scar was left behind by the bottle I used on Mike's head six years earlier. For a moment, I regretted not finishing him that night.

The sound of the fan on the projector in the room got louder. The doctor's voice, the crying family, the donation coordinator. They all fell silent. I searched. I was fearful at first. I was afraid that I wouldn't be able to come back. I was not going to let Mike do this. If anyone would burn, the sociopathic faggot who stole my father away from me would be first in line.

I opened my eyes. I found it. Neutral. The state of mind came to me. The dark place where I could operate without yet emulate any emotion I needed to. Mike had unwittingly turned me into himself. I had learned every single narcissistic play in his book. He no longer owned me. I owned myself. I could outwit, outsmart, outcharm, and outplay him. I was going to begin a session of his own game. And then I would beat him. I would lead him into his own demise. I would watch him choke on the pieces.

My grandparents, my aunts, and my mother deserved to tie off their relationship with my father without Mike Burton pulling the strings. My motivation wasn't purely charitable. I wanted my father back. I wanted the dad that my father was before he met Mike Burton. I wanted to rewrite my childhood. I wasn't going to get any of that. What I could get was control. I could obtain from Mike Burton what he never deserved to own in the first place.

I spoke.

"Mike, I'm scared. I don't want to worry about that stuff right now. We are both in the same boat. I'm just so grateful you are still here. Dad didn't leave us totally alone. I guess that's one of the unique perks of having two dads. Love ya, Mike."

"Love you too, buddy," Mike said. "Let's just get some time to figure out what we are gonna do."

With a reassuring embrace smelling of rat urine and vodka, I enjoyed the victory. I was inside his head. Mike Burton now had a copilot to deal with. Now it would require two people to land his plane.

Chapter 12

Bridges

2012

We arrived at the apartment in Pleasant Grove. I walked in the door. In the kitchen, I saw remnants of the chaotic history between mike and my father. Shards of glass that had evaded sweeping, cracks in baseboards, amateur patches in drywall. All were artifacts that reminded me of what day to day life was like with my father and Mike Burton. They also foreshadowed what would come if I was to move to Oregon with Mike and Dad.

I already spent several nights on park benches. I knew that was not a note I wanted to end my childhood on. The only option for me was to admit to myself and my mother that I had made a mistake. I heard that she had gotten clean. I wanted to believe it. Now, my desire turned into a necessity. I had to believe it. I had nowhere to go.

I went to my room and prepared my go-bag. I also prepared mentally to burn my father. The battle for my father was about to end. Mike Burton would soon gain a victory. Mike would win my father and cut every last string attached to him. For the second time, my father would abandon me. I decided to let him.

I dropped any and all attachment I had to my father. If he could disown me twice, I couldn't see anything prohibiting me from washing my hands of him. My father forced me into a corner. I had spent so long with a father that fostered what I deemed to be binary love. Either my father loved me, or he didn't. I grew weary. I did not want to burn another bridge, only to have to be the one to rebuild it again in the future. It was too hard. Too taxing.

I realized on my seventeenth birthday, when my father told me he was moving to Oregon with Mike, that he did love me. However, he loved Mike Burton more. I knew that it wasn't a case of Dad loving himself more than me.

I could see Dad hated himself. He was miles off the beaten path. He couldn't find his way back. Only alcohol could medicate and dull his pain and regret. Mike Burton's affection offered an artificial substance for my father's heart to consume. Like vegan ice cream, it had a correct appearance, but with every lick, it was clearer that hand-churned old-fashioned ice cream was not in Dad's cone. True love was not in Mike Burton's heart. I knew I could not protest against my father's decision or relationship. After all, who knocks ice cream out of a child's hand? I had to let him go.

I prayed that eventually the artificial nature of Mike Burton would crack, and my father would come to his senses. I mourned the loss of my father to Mike Burton. I recalled that day, almost a year before when I was introduced to Mike Burton. I remembered studying him. The first thing that came to mind was the thought, "I am going to lose Dad to this man."

Mom's number was blocked in the cell phone my father provided me. I took a walk. My hand rubbed against my blue jeans. My second cell phone was sheathed in my pocket. It was ready to be used in a battle for my future. My fingers started to flirt with the gray brick of plastic.

Stacey's phone rang. It was provoked by an incoming call from an unknown number. Since the divorce, she had been harassed by bill collectors and lawyers. Stacey would have ignored the call, but today was a bad day; she felt like yelling. After shifting into a gear suitable for fighting, she drew in a breath and answered the call.

"Who is this?" Stacey said. She was careful not to give her name out before she knew who was trying to reach her.

"Hi, Mom. It's Kameron. Your son. Can you talk?" I was approaching a woman who I had put through hell. I had burned the relationship and scattered the ashes. Only she hadn't burned anything. To her, the relationship with her son was a bleeding artery. My absence was the jagged knife that had pierced her. If she did anything to try and remove it, she would bleed out. For the past year, she had lived her life alone and impaled. Fear of doing further damage kept her at bay. Petrified by the prospect of losing her son forever, she let me stay with my father. Little did I know, Mom had been patiently waiting to provide me safe harbor for quite some time.

She also had a lot of information which was not available to me. I was surprised at the lucid and sober manner in which she was talking. This was a woman who was not stoned. Her voice was clear and concise. She was alert and ready for battle with an unknown adversary on the other end of a phone line. In my mind, she'd just passed a random drug screening. This did not match up with what dad had been telling me for eight months.

"Yes, sure! What's up?" She didn't skip a beat. Though she sounded perfectly casual, Stacey had been waiting and praying for her son to make contact for almost a year. Finally, contact. Her son's voice. She could only hope, but her head was screaming with anticipation and fear. Could this be the day? Would he come to his senses? Did he find out that his father had been manipulating him this whole time? Would he have enough trust in her to come back? Or did his father actually break him? Was this a final goodbye?

"Uh, so, could I come over to your place for a while? Things with dad are...complicated. I just—can you? Would you be okay if—" I did not know what to say. How does one rebuild a relationship so close yet so adamantly damned by oneself? I was embarrassed. I was scared. I felt so stupid and helpless. I was crawling back on my knees after hurting her in the worst way that a mother can be harmed—by her own child.

"Kameron, it's okay. You're fine. Come on over if you want to. We can talk if you want. If you don't want to talk, that's fine too. Whatever you need, just let me know. I am here." Stacey was able to smoothly reply, though on the inside, her heart was doing summersaults. After so long, he finally called. He wanted to talk. It would be hard to conceal the pain, but above all, she just wanted her son back.

"Okay, I gotta go pretty soon, but thanks for talking. Let's get together soon. Love you."

"Love you too," Stacey replied.

It was harder to live with myself after that call. I realized she had been fine during the entire time that I had lived with Dad and Mike Burton. Little did I know that my father's manipulation tactics took root deep into my reality. Everything I thought I knew about my mother's situation was engineered. I was being used. I was being used hard. Ripping a woman's heart out is nothing compared to ripping a mother's child away. My father knew it. So did Mike Burton.

2018
July 22, Sunday, 1:00 p.m.

The meeting wrapped up. Everyone agreed to leave the decision for another day. We all needed rest. Making decisions and thinking in the frame of mind that we all were in was not productive. Grandma and Grandpa went home. So did Katie and Michelle. I went down to Carla's house. On my way, the fatigue caught up with me. I had traveled ten miles down the freeway. I was alone with my thoughts.

As I started to drift off, I thought I heard Dad say, "Kam, might want to pull over." I thought I was just tired, and I only had twenty more miles left until Carla's house. Of course, it was normal to hear things after exhaustion. I would be fine. I shook myself awake and focused on the center lane. My eyelids were weighted; it took all I had to keep them open. I just needed to get to Carla's house, and then I could sleep twelve hours. I looked to my right, about to doze off. In the rear passenger side seat, Dad said again, "KAMERON, WAKE UP! PULL OFF THE ROAD NOW." His left hand shoved into my right shoulder. My head straightened out. My foot slammed on the brake. The Volvo semitruck I had been tailgating suddenly stopped after being cut off by a red Miata. I was still about twelve miles from Carla's house. I took the next exit. The first right turn led me into a parking lot of an office complex. When I opened my eyes, it was 10:00 p.m. Seven hours had passed since I had left the hospital. I drove on an empty freeway to Carla's house to sleep in her guest room.

Chapter 13

Pursuit of Happiness

2014

January. I walked down to the terminal and saw Uncle Tyler waiting with a reassuring smile. He greeted me with open arms and asked if my flight went well. I replied, "Went fine." I was petrified. For the first time in years, I would be living in an unbroken home. I wasn't exactly an indoor dog anymore. I had forgotten many of the comforts of a family, such as sitting around a dinner table—enjoying each other's company.

I woke up the next morning to the sound of a knock on the guest room door.

"Time for scriptures!" I heard my little cousin Matthew yell through the door.

"Huh? Okay, I'll be right down," I replied, still sleepy. I staggered through the upstairs hallway. My feet found the stairs before my brain did, and I slipped down five steps before I caught myself. I found the family of four sitting in the living room together. Uncle Tyler pulled out his scriptures. He read from the Book of Mormon.

I was raised in the Church of Jesus Christ of Latter-Day Saints. Most of my family was LDS. After Dad left the church, I pretty much left too. I wasn't really on the best of terms with God. And I didn't really have much desire to fix the relationship with him. I figured that I was going to die soon anyway, I could set things right when I was face to face with the big man.

Out of respect for Aunt Sharon and Uncle Tyler, I adjusted some of my behaviors. I stopped using foul language, and I changed my lifestyle to better fit the health code. Goodbye, coffee. I figured going without my beloved iced caramel macchiato was a small sacrifice for a second shot at life. It was incredibly ironic that I had to give up coffee to move to the Starbucks capital of the world.

The next four months, I feared I would be out of my element. I had no idea that I was in training. I was training and preparing for a future that I thought would never come. The pure normalcy of that household was the alkaline to my acidic past. In my time there, the odds were very low that I would encounter broken bottles or domestic violence cases. Uncle Tyler and Aunt Sharon's home exuded love and harmony. For the first time in a long time, I saw what a functional family looked like.

2018
July 23, Monday, 9:00 a.m.

We were all in agreement that the machines needed to be turned off. Dad was gone. He was not coming back. The handling of his body postmortem was still undecided. It wasn't an immediate concern. Keeping the machines on wouldn't do anything. It would perhaps buy me more time with Mike Burton. But I knew better. I also knew Mike. More time wasn't always a beneficial asset to provide to him. It was easy to manipulate Mike Burton. History had taught me that the best time to get inside his head was when he felt like he didn't have time to evaluate.

Dad wasn't coming back. His organs were coveted by the donation coordinator. I needed to increase the pressure on Mike Burton. It served my interests well to become a strong advocate for turning off the machines as soon as possible.

I commandeered the conversation. I had Dad's family on my side. I pinned Mike. I had him surrounded. He was intimidated. If anyone else provoked him, I knew he would pull rank. I had to be the one piloting the conversation. I looked him in the eyes. I weighed in on what the course of action should be. We would pull support from my father at 10:00 a.m. We all spent time with my father both individually and as a group. The organ harvesting team stood by. After life departed from Dad, the medical staff would have only minutes to act before the organs would cease to be viable.

The nurses turned off the machines, switch by switch, the man-made army resigned from their stations. The final means of artificial life to be removed was the tubing pulled from his throat. Dad continued to breathe on his own for approximately two minutes and thirty seconds.

His voice still could be heard in the vocal cords vibrating in the body. It struggled to provide the organs with oxygen. A process that this body had been engaged in, nonstop from the time of my father's birth, ceased. Bile came up out of his mouth. He aspirated. Dad was gone. We stepped aside as the staff unlocked the wheels of the bed. They rushed Dad's lifeless body out of the room.

Everyone remained in the room standing around the heart-breaking void, which was left behind. I followed the bed. I turned and ran out the doorway. I was then pushed aside. I looked to my right. I watched as my father chased after the bed as if a warrior sprinting into battle. I found a peculiar comfort in the vision. For much of my father's life, he was a conflicted man. Looking to come to the aid of other people, only to deem himself incapable.

The last time I saw my father, he was trying to facilitate the acceptance of his organs into another person. I turned and walked back to the hospital room. It was noticeable that dad was not present. I seemed to be the only one who knew that he had merely changed rooms. I wondered how many people had been wheeled down that hallway.

Chapter 14

Like a Hole in the Head

2014

May. For five months my mind trod through a green cemetery. Every day, my procession drew nearer to a specific grave. I knew the grave in my mind's eye would likely be mine. The actual process of obtaining, inhabiting, and using a grave was quite simple.

A warm day would permit a grave to be opened in forty-five minutes to an hour. The funeral would wrap up, and everyone would leave. The gravedigger would return to his backhoe and replace the soil over my casket. The ground would be lightly compacted. A few months later, a modest headstone would rest six feet above my body to mark that the plot was occupied.

I was closer than ever to finishing that daydream. When the neurologist told us that I was a candidate for an invasive EEG, I stood at the foot of my own grave. I waited for something to come along and push me in. The week before I went into the hospital was a blur.

The last neurologist appointment was unusual. Dr. Stafford came into the exam room and asked us to follow him into his office. Sharon and I looked at each other, puzzled. He led us into his corner office and gestured to the bright yellow midcentury modern sofa facing his desk. We sat down.

Stafford began. "Kameron, your MRI results came back. From what we see, the only way out of this is to keep going forward. I have determined that the next course of action, if you are willing, is an invasive EEG."

I replied, "So what exactly are you saying? Am I a candidate for surgery?"

Stafford was hesitant to reply as he tried to bond the right words together. "We cannot determine what the best course of action will be until we get up close to your brain. Real close. Imagine that your brain is trying to tell us what is wrong, but right now, it is in a soundproofed room.

We can put a cup up to the door and listen, but so far, all we have gotten is mumbling. We know that your brain is asking for help. But we cannot understand what your brain is trying to tell us unless we open the door and let it talk directly to us. Does that make sense?"

Trying to get out of the metaphor, I said, "My skull is the door."

Dr. Stafford was delighted that his euphemized description of brain surgery clicked in my head. "Precisely. What would happen is we will temporarily remove a portion of your skull over the right frontal lobe. Then we cut and peel back the dura, which is a thick membrane that protects your brain. Once we have that out of the way, we can place a grid of electrodes directly onto the surface of your brain. That grid will detect any abnormal electrical activity. We take you off all your meds and monitor you during your seizures over the course of a week in the hospital. With that data, we can pinpoint exactly what the problem area is. If it is operable, we will resect the damaged area after we remove the grid. You only have to be opened and closed up once."

I began to get excited. "Sounds pretty simple! It's not like it's a brain…oh, it is." Things were beginning to sink in.

Stafford appreciated the humor. He countered in an effort to build rapport. "Here, yes, it is a pretty routine surgery. It doesn't happen too often in the ortho unit though." He chuckled.

"You said the goal was to eliminate, as in cure?" I was trying to picture a life without epilepsy.

Dr. Stafford's confidence seemed to grow. "We have some of the best neurosurgeons in the country. If you can be cured of your seizures, this is the place to come. We need to manage expectations though. We won't know what the best course of action will be until we get the data."

He was right. I replied, "It sounds like a no-brainer to me! Let's go. Let's do this."

He responded with comfort. "All right, Kameron, we'll get you on the schedule."

Sharon and I looked at each other, astonished that we were actually at this point. We drove home. The traffic was horrible as always, but today I didn't mind.

I thought about all the things that I had learned due to Aunt Sharon's insistent push for me to learn different life skills. Skills I thought were a waste. I wouldn't have a life to use them in for much longer.

Maybe I would have a need to navigate a big city like Seattle on my own in the future, as I had for the last few months by Sharon's command. Maybe I would have a job interview that would favor the Microsoft certifications that, thanks to Uncle Tyler, I now had on my résumé.

Maybe, just maybe—the last months of my life I'd spent in Seattle weren't wasted. Now there was a real chance that these skills could possibly be invested in a future. A future that only nine months earlier had been condemned. Little did I know that I would be on a table for surgery prep in a week.

Years of waiting and months of hope had come to this. Aunt Sharon had navigated the impossible labyrinth of medical insurance. She brought me through the other side. I had undergone testing, doctors' appointments, and deteriorating health for months. The moment I was waiting for was here. I looked up at Tyler. He looked down at me and wished me luck.

As I was lying in the hospital bed, I reflected on how I had lived my life. After all, there was a chance that I wouldn't get any more life. A chance that I would be transferred from the operating room via body bag.

I wondered about how small the slots of the refrigerators in the morgue were. I was claustrophobic as hell. My worst nightmare would be to wake up in one of those morgue refrigerators. Did they have an escape handle on the inside, just in case?

I definitely wanted a bell with a string on it put through my grave. Though it may never be used, the bell offered peace of mind. I told Aunt Sharon as much. I shifted my body around in the hospital bed, and I hoped that if I didn't make it out alive that a casket would be more comfortable than the bed I was in. What if back pain followed me to the other side?

I thought about the letters that I wrote to my parents. I hoped that I said the right things. I wouldn't have to live much longer with what my final words were. But they would have a lot more time than me to contemplate the relationship. My mother hadn't called me in seven months. My father and I had stopped talking shortly after he left for Oregon two years before. He didn't even know I was less than a three-hour drive from Portland. Or in a hospital. Or that I had received a terminal diagnosis. He made his peace with the relationship dying when he left. What difference would it make whether I was alive or not? I was fine with the postal service conveying my last words.

I recounted the time that I had spent with my father and Mike Burton. My biggest regret was the harm that I did to everyone around me while I was living with them.

I should have given more, tried more, been smarter. I hated myself for being manipulated. My relationship with my mother was never the same. My relationship with Carla was never the same. I wished that I hadn't braced for impact.

I was able to see my childhood with a bird's eye view. I had an amazing family. Then I turned eleven. I saw the subtle signs preceding the crash. The plane losing altitude. The point where I saw the oxygen masks drop from the cabin ceiling. I was too selfish. I put on my own oxygen mask first.

The stewardess always preaches to put on your own oxygen mask first. The fewer people die, the fewer lawsuits the airline gets. It makes financial sense for the airline to adopt that policy.

But what happens to the people that can't put on their own mask? What do they do? The only thing that they can do is wait. Wait for someone to come along and help.

I was the only person near my parents on the flight. They didn't know how to put on the mask. I chose to brace for impact instead of helping them.

The anesthesiologist placed the mask over my face. Oxygen was not the gas going through me. This gas would ferry me through a traumatic wound which would hopefully lead to a brighter future, albeit with a great deal of healing and pain. Ultimately it was the only way to joy. I breathed in and started to count.

I remembered Mom and Dad. We were sitting in the living room. The tree was lit. We were laughing. Playing Mario Kart on the Nintendo 64 that Santa had brought me the night before. I couldn't remember who won. I knew that even though eventually we would all lose, the joy of playing the game in the moment was an emotion that could be called upon in times of darkness after the final game. A princess, a plumber, and a green dinosaur would race through various courses before the game turned off.

I got to the number 8 and closed my eyes. The fluorescent lights of the hallway leading to the operating room were so bright. Then they were gone. Darkness.

2018
July 23, Monday, 10:30 a.m.

We left the hospital and sought nourishment. The first family meal that my grandparents organized after their son's death was hosted by an Olive Garden. I recalled the last time we went to Olive Garden together. It was for my seventeenth birthday. The occasion also served as a perfect time for Dad and Mike Burton to announce they were moving to Oregon. Suffice it to say, I was filled with mixed emotions for the venue. We were seated by a waitress named Jennie. Her fake enthusiasm was palpable. She probably felt that the position would soon be far beneath her once she finished her hospitality management degree.

Jennie, the waitress, asked us habitually, "So, guys, are we celebrating today?"

I cut in before any other response had a chance to fertilize in anybody's head. "We are celebrating a life. My father just passed away this morning. The hospital cafeteria is a bit depressing, and the food there is dog shit. I think I'll start with some chicken gnocchi soup and iced water to drink."

Michelle looked at me and gave a nonverbal expression of gratitude for me speaking first and breaking the ice. Everyone proceeded to order as the confounded waitress named Jennie took notes on a pad with a black Pilot G2. When I saw the pen, I smiled. Dad would only write with those pens. He turned me onto them and passed the affinity for the pen to me. At first, we tried to make small talk to pass the time before the food came.

What began as small talk turned into exchanges of memories, largely critical, about my father. Regarding his fastidious recordkeeping or the care he would take to remember birthdays. Childhood memories of Michael. It was sweet. For the longest time, I hadn't been a part of this family. When Dad left for Oregon, I was still a reminder of the relationship that they lost.

It was painful and awkward for them. It was disappointing to me that I couldn't have a relationship with the Parkins, independent of my father. Now that Dad was dead, it left us no choice. To my surprise, they actually clung onto me, as if I was all they had left of Michael. Likewise, I clung to them. They were all I had left of Dad.

A spam e-mail vibrated my phone. When I looked at the notification, I drifted into the camera roll on my phone. I looked at the last photos of my father. I saw the surgical incision on his head, held together with staples. I recalled the time when I had similar staples removed from my skull.

Chapter 15

In Stitches

2014

June. Darkness faded. I saw blue walls. Dark walls. I felt like I should be in pain. But I wasn't. I had an IV. I liked the IV. The IV was good. It made things good. I thought that maybe they could let me take it home like a souvenir cup. I didn't know what was in the IV, but I knew that it was cool. I wanted to live there.

I saw that there was a TV on the wall, and I could control it with my bed remote. I wondered what else I could control with the remote. I could move the bed up and down. Maybe I could drive the bed with the remote. There had to be a gas pedal somewhere. I couldn't find the damn ignition though. The heater wasn't working either. I did see that there was a call button. I called the nurse in to tell me how to start the stupid bed. When she came into the room, I complained.

She asked, "Hello. How are you feeling? Do you know where you are?"

I responded with annoyance. "Well, What's your name again?"

"My name is Tami, sir. do you know where you are?"

I replied, "Tami, I am in the hospital. In a hospital bed. The president is Barack Obama. The date is sometime in June 2014. My name is Kameron Parkin, born May '95. Good enough?

"Good enough, Kameron," Tami said. How is your pain?"

I replied. "I don't care about my pain, Tami. I just want to start my bed so I can get out of here. And I can't find the keys or the ignition. Can you tell me where it is?"

She expertly countered. "Mr. Parkin, you just had surgery, and the anesthesia is still wearing off. Until I see that it's out of your system, I can't let you drive your bed. I'm sorry. Is there anything else that I can do for you?"

Just then, I noticed that my head was very heavy. "Surgery, huh? Oh, that's right."

I will let Dr. Stafford know you are awake. He will be in momentarily," Tami said.

"Okay," I replied. I was too afraid to move. I remembered that I had head surgery; there was a grid on my brain. A piece of my skull was missing. In a refrigerator somewhere. My heart rate started to go up as the doctor came into my room.

"Kameron! How are you doing? Tami tells me you are still a bit sleepy from the anesthesia. Don't worry, that's normal. Some people take a bit longer to come out of it than others," Dr. Stafford said.

"My head feels really heavy. Why is it heavy? Did something go wrong?" I was still a bit scared but comforted by Dr. Stafford's demeanor.

Stafford replied, "The procedure went off without a hitch. The grid is in place and you did just fine. Now we can monitor you and get your brain to talk face to face with us. We can figure exactly what is wrong. After we go through the data, we can talk options! Right now, just get some rest. Your body just went through a lot, and you need to recover."

My head still felt like it weighed twice as much as before the surgery. "How big is this grid?" I reached up.

"I wouldn't do that if I were you," Stafford warned. He got a mirror and showed me my head. "You are connected to this monitor over here on the cart. These cables feed your brain's data directly into this, and we can map your seizures with it."

He handed me the mirror. I was a sight to behold. It definitely explained the weight. My head was wrapped tightly in a long white bandage. Data ribbon cables fed out the top of my head like a desktop computer. I was connected to a monitor. Hell, I was a human desktop computer. I asked Dr. Stafford, "If I eat apple sauce, will I boot into Mac OS X?"

He chuckled and said, "Worth a shot. Right now, let's just save some memory and get some rest."

I did have an actual concern. "Dr. Stafford, you said you are taking me off my meds and want me to have seizures. Exactly how much extra length is there in these cables? Is there a breakaway or something?"

He replied and pointed down at the rails on the bed. "Don't worry about that, we've accounted for it. There is enough slack and reinforcement in the connections. Your safety is of the utmost concern. The point is to have seizures. But they will be in a safe environment you don't have to worry about hurting yourself in. Of all the places to have a seizure, this is likely the only place that you will have zero injury as a result. We have a full medical staff monitoring you. Your vitals are connected to an alert system, and you are on camera. We won't miss a thing."

What I was afraid would be a long week, actually was the shortest week of my life. Before I knew it, I had sixty-three seizures and they had mapped the exact area in my right frontal lobe which needed to be removed. It was in fact deemed operable. Dr. Stafford discussed with me what exactly I was putting at stake to pursue surgery. There would be a chance that I would lose mobility. I could lose speech. My memory could be affected. The surgery might not work. And of course, there was a risk of death.

There was a certainty of death if I left. Joe passed away during the week I was in the hospital. The family experienced enough death. I chose to face the possibility of a long life with a disability. A short life without limits had less potential than a long life with a limit.

I signed the papers. They booked me for surgery the next morning. I would have my right frontal lobe resected. I reflected once again on the letters I wrote my parents.

Dear Dad,

If you are receiving this letter, I am gone. I know we had our differences. We had our highs. We had our lows. It is unfortunate that we ended on a low. But know that through it all, I still loved you. I know you still loved me.

Sometimes priorities have a way of slipping out of grasp. I want you to know that I went through a lot at your hands. You lost me to death, but I lost you long before the postmark on the envelope this letter came in.

If I had one do-over—it would be to cut between you and Mike when I had the chance. The day will come when you will see Mike for what he truly is. Now, you won't have anybody to catch you. That scares me. Maybe if I did something earlier, you would have me to support you. Find happiness. Find love like you used to know.

Kameron

Dear Mom,

If you are reading this, you are probably crying. Stop it. You will be fine. We have definitely had our highs and lows. Yes, I *am* going to make that joke—because I'm dead and you can't give me that death glare. I am sorry for everything I have done to you. I am sorry I called you a shitty mother. I'm sorry about the lies that I told, the secrets I kept. Even though It felt amazing at the time and I got a crazy amount of adrenaline from it. I'm also sorry for that time I called you a bitch and told you to fuck off. Because of that I'm most likely on my way to the island in Pinocchio where all the bad sons go. But most of all, I am sorry for eating entire bags of teriyaki beef jerky from your stash while you were asleep when I was a kid. I know there is a lot to say and neither of us will get the chance to say it. But the time that I did have was real. I want you to know that even though you made mistakes as a mother and I sure as hell made mistakes as a son, I wouldn't trade it for the world. You were the perfect mother for me. You turned me into the person I was at the end. I wasn't the greatest to people. But I think I was a likable son of a bitch. I credit that to you.

Kameron

2018
July 23, Monday, 2:00 p.m.

I sat in my car and watched the Parkins leave the Olive Garden Parking lot. After inhaling and exhaling through my nose, I picked my phone up from the dashboard. I looked in my contacts and saw his name. It was time to go to the scene of the accident. I pursed my lips, cleared my throat, and tapped Mike Burton's number.

He answered, "Hey, Kam. What's happening'?"

He was drunk.

I dug through my bag of emotions. When I found the correct "mask," I replied as a damsel in emotional distress. "Oh, nothing. Just trying to get through the day. I keep trying to keep myself distracted, but it's not working. What are you doing?"

He replied, "I know, I tried to do the same thing for a while."

"Where are you? Maybe we can be distracted together."

"I'm at my place, but I think I am gonna go out to a few bars or something."

I was quick to cut in. "I'll go with you. You shouldn't drink alone right now."

He countered. "Kameron, you don't drink!"

"I know. But I can order Shirley Temples and be your designated driver!"

It took him a second to find a way out. "Actually, buddy, I am already pretty fucked up. I have been drinking all day. I might just stay home."

Even better. I wanted to get into the apartment. "Okay, how 'bout this, I'll come over, and we will do a Robin Williams Marathon. We can order Chinese."

"I haven't eaten since before your dad went into the hospital." I was cracking him.

I smiled. "Okay, well if you've been drinking, we definitely need to get some food into you."

He sighed. "Fine. but if you come over, I am still going to be drinking. *No judging, okay?* I am drunk, and I want to stay drunk, and I don't need the drink police to say I have had enough. I swear to God, I will kick you out if you get bitchy with me."

I had him. I was in. Worst-case scenario, I would bash his head in with another vodka bottle and walk away. I smiled and continued. "Mike, I think of all the times in your life to get fucked up, it's tonight. *No* judgment. I just don't think either one of us should be alone right now."

"You're probably right. Okay. Come on up."

Another win. I would be able to see where my father was injured with my own eyes. A privilege that would never come to anyone else that was close to my father.

I closed the phone call. "All-righty, I'll be up in a bit. Love ya." The expression of love burned the roof of my mouth. Saying that I cared for that snake affected me like I was vomiting a freshly prepared caramel macchiato. The caramel was once sweet, now tasted of bile. The milk and vanilla now curdled and sour. The coffee burned and scarred me on its way up my throat leaving a trail of bitterness.

Luckily, I had enough emotional distance from him that I could rinse him away. I would expel Mike from my life. When I soon could forget that he was even a part of it. But tonight, I needed him. I looked eagerly to the future when Mike would be expendable—a worthless serpent in the allegory of my past.

I arrived at the apartment and came to his door. With three knocks and a considerable pause, Mike slithered to the door. He stumbled out into the hallway and hugged me. He wreaked of rum and vodka.

When I got inside, a deceased and forgotten part of me awakened and instantly felt at home. The apartment had all the hallmarks to be expected in a dwelling shared by my dad and Mike Burton. Cracked baseboards, patched drywall—it was all there. I knew exactly what happened. I just needed to confirm.

Mike hadn't bothered to take out the trash. I peered into it as he poured himself another drink. Sure enough, there were two empty bottles of Skyy in the bottom of the can—fighting booze. I looked back up at the apartment. I saw the barstool that my father supposedly fell off of.

Mike Burton went to the bathroom to loudly relieve himself. I took the opportunity to examine the barstool when I noticed a piece of molding hanging off the doorway as if something heavy had hit into it. I had seen enough to realize there was a fight.

I was the only person to see that apartment that knew their history. Something happened in order to cause Dad to pass out on the carpet on which I stood. I looked around the room. I was surrounded by every single hallmark of Mike Burton's brand of domestic violence.

As I heard Mike Burton dribbling in the bathroom, I labeled him as a very lucky man.

There was a time when I had nothing to lose. I had eighteen months—give or take—to live. I didn't care what I would find in the afterlife. I wouldn't live long enough to see prison.

Mike Burton and I had caused multiple scars on each other's bodies and minds. He infected part of me with an evil far more refined and purer than he would ever manifest in himself.

I could end him right there. With a few more hours of pouring drinks, getting him one drink away from passing out would be simple. A trip to his medicine cabinet would certainly provide me with a fatal mixer—easy as picking up a used car from a dealer and filling it with gas.

When I stood in Mike Burton's living room, I did possess something. I had everything. I won. I had a life. I had family. I had love.

I possessed more than Mike Burton would ever attain in life. Killing him wasn't an option—anymore. I didn't have to send him to hell. He was driving himself there.

As I drove back to Carla's house, I tried to discern why I abandoned Mike Burton. Was it out of mercy? Was it out of honor? Was it out of selfishness? I didn't quite know. But I knew that rising above Mike Burton was the only way for me to end Mike Burton.

Chapter 16

Return

2014

August. Six weeks passed since my surgery. I was out of rehab. I was strong, and I was seizure-free. The surgery worked. My expiration date had been revoked, and I no longer possessed the comfort of certain death. Nobody would have understood my feelings. I just won a proverbial lottery. I beat the odds and won my life back. A clean bill of health was a beautiful thing indeed. To me, it was far more daunting than a death certificate.

Sharon decided to make a road trip out of the venture of returning me to Utah. Everything was loaded into her dark grey Honda Odyssey. We set out on the road toward my home—at least the place I called home. I didn't know what I would return to. I knew that I wouldn't find Joe there.

From the passenger seat in the minivan, I stared out the windshield. Once again, I found myself looking down a road. This road had an end. It led to where I came from. I would be back at Carla's home in twelve hours.

I owed it to Tyler and Sharon and myself to not waste my second chance. If I was going to be successful, I had to get out on my own. I had to get a job. I had to start a life. Aunt Sharon's voice was in my head. Over and over again, I couldn't get her question out of my head. "What do you want out of life, Kameron?" I wanted happiness. I wanted freedom. I wanted independence. I had no idea how to obtain those things. I knew I couldn't get anything while I was living in Carla's basement. I gave myself a month.

A week after I came back from Washington, I had a job. My first day of training was terrible. I knew telemarketing was not a good fit, but it was money. Money paved a road that led to a future. My commute included two miles a day on my bike and a ten-mile bus ride.

Day four of my first job. What began as ten hires was cut down to six. Kathy, Meghan, Jessica, Tim, Victor, and I made the cut. We began our shift making cold calls. After seven hours of cold calls, on a Friday, I wanted to choke myself with the cable connecting my headset to the computer.

I wanted to get home and sleep the entire weekend away. Key already in hand, I went for the cable lock securing my bike. My rear tire had gone completely flat. Victor was parked across the aisle from me.

He looked over at me as I was muttering and cursing. "What's wrong? Your bike is flat?"

"Yeah, it appears to be." I would have to wait another hour at the bus stop. I was visibly angry at the universe.

Victor pointed at the bicycle mount on the back of his car. "You want a ride?"

"Really?" I was surprised. Maybe the universe wasn't so mean.

"Yeah, sure. Where do you live?" he asked.

I knew that he would try to back out when I told him. "I live off Sixth Street and Twelfth West." It was well out of his way.

"Okay, sure! Do you mind if I stop by my apartment first, I'm going out with some friends, and I need to grab a few things. I'll just drop you off on the way."

"Yeah, absolutely. Thanks so much!" I found a way home. And made a new friend. It wasn't such a bad wrap to the week after all.

We arrived at Victor's apartment. "Do you want to come up or wait out here? I might be a minute," Victor asked.

"Sure, I'll come up." I was curious to see how someone my age was supposed to live.

We rode the elevator to the 3rd floor of his building. When I followed him through the front door of his student apartment, I was surprised by what I saw. His apartment was very livable. He did have a shared room, but the living space was quite decent. I started to get curious.

After all, we had the same source of income. I knew exactly what Victor brought home each week. It certainly wasn't much, but his miniscule check could put him into the apartment I was standing in. There wasn't any reason that my miniscule paycheck couldn't do the same. At the risk of being rude, I asked, "Hey, nice place. Just out of curiosity, what do they charge for a room here? I'm thinking about moving, and I can't find a place I like."

"My rent is $325 including utilities. It is a shared room. But I don't mind it. The rooms are pretty big."

I did some quick math in my head as I responded. "Oh, cool. Utilities included, That's pretty good."

Yeah, I like it. It's pretty new construction. Low maintenance." Victor appeared to be very content with the apartment.

I began to formulate my plan. I saw a way out. I had to bring it to fruition. I had a job. It was time to get out.

We arrived at Carla's house. I retrieved my bike from the back of Victor's car. "Thank you again, Victor!"

"Don't mention it. See you Monday!"

I rolled my bike into the carport. I'd deal with the repair tomorrow. I grabbed a notebook and pen out of my desk. I sat down with a calculator in hand.

I made about $400 per week after taxes. I started the list with the assumption that I made $1,600 a month—$100 for my phone, $60 for my bus pass, $120 for groceries, $325 for rent. The bare essentials left me with $995—nearly $1,000 per month. I thought nearly a thousand bucks was a decent buffer. I could do it.

In the morning, I repaired my flat tire, and I rode my bike to Victor's apartment complex. The leasing office was open. Sherri, the leasing agent took me on a tour. She boasted about the building's amenities—a pool, a gym, a restaurant. What Sherri didn't know was that I was ready to sign before we got in the elevator.

2018
July 24, Tuesday, 7:00 a.m.

I stared up at the ceiling from the bed—the bed that once belonged to my grandfather. I still was haunted by the thoughts my mind entertained the night before.

The morning light began to leak through the window blinds. I looked over at my phone—6:58 a.m. In two minutes, the phone would blare that damned xylophone alarm. I took the opportunity to silence the phone before it could have its fun. I looked back up the ceiling.

Fingers interlaced behind my head, I pondered what exactly separated me from Mike Burton. Dad was gone. He left me with Mike Burton. Whenever I needed my dad, Mike Burton monopolized his time. It felt like a lifetime since the last time I was truly alone with Dad. Waking up that day, in that bed, I just needed to talk with him one last time. I needed dad to talk back.

My phone started to vibrate on the nightstand. I looked over to see Mike Burton was attempting to call me. I wasn't ready to deal with him. I held the phone in my hand and waited as the phone continued to vibrate. Mike's call was interrupted by a notification. It was a reward notification from Costa Vida—one of dad's favorite haunts.

At one time, we used to meet there weekly for lunch. Whenever a fight was about to break out or negative tension was building, Dad would say, "Time out! Burrito break!"

The pressure to answer Mike Burton fell away with the offer for a discount burrito. Almost as if Dad were using my phone to advise me to ignore Mike Burton. I decided to go with it. I felt like in some way, Dad was there with me.

I took a shower. After I got ready for the day, I got in the car. I didn't know where I was going, but I knew that I couldn't stay at Carla's house all day. I had no plan for the day. I was hoping to have a little bit of help. Ten minutes later, I found myself parked in front of a thrift store. Of course, it had to be a thrift store.

Dad's signature remedy for sadness was shopping. In his later years as his wallet got thinner, he shifted his efforts toward "vintage apparel." I had my car with me, and I wouldn't be flying back to California. Technically, I could buy something and have room to take it home with me. Maybe something in the store would remind me of Dad. I may find something like he used to own. Or maybe I would find something on my thrift list, my list of items that I would buy on the spot if I found them secondhand.

I walked in the door of the thrift store. My nose was bombarded by the distinct yet unidentifiable smell that was universal across all thrift stores. It was musty at first, then hints of alcohol-based cleaners mixed in. The different scents danced with each other down the aisles of clothing, children's toys, and household goods.

I strolled through the store, section by section in my prioritized order.

"Furniture." It wasn't likely hell would freeze over, but if it did, I wanted to enjoy the winter storm from a secondhand Eames Lounge chair, with a midcentury modern stereo console playing in the background.

"Electronics." Every once in a while, a fellow audiophile would die. Their loved ones unwittingly throw out thousands of dollars' worth of stereo equipment.

"Clothing." Armed with my father's knowledge of designer lines, if I was lucky, I could score a high-quality suit or a new messenger bag.

"Books & Media." I might not find Blu-ray discs, but there were hundreds of great movies on VHS to be had for nickels. With a professional grade VCR, they would play at DVD quality.

The thrift store's inventory was sparse. Floral couches dominated the furniture section. Countless discarded waffle irons, toasters, and coffee mugs lined the shelves in household goods. Tube TVs were plugged in and waiting for someone to rent *The Princess Bride* just one last time. Oversized and outdated suitcoats and dresses dominated the clothing racks. Maybe just maybe, I would find a gem in shelves of books and movies.

I walked to the sign hanging from the ceiling. It read "Media." Cassette tapes, VHS tapes, CDs, DVDs, books, records. It seemed like everything in this store was trash. While thumbing through the tapes, my hand stopped. In the middle of the dozens of VHS tapes, there they were. Two copies right next to each other. *Jack Frost*—probably the corniest and most forgettable Christmas movie ever produced. It also happened to be the last holiday movie I watched with Dad. As if a tender sign that he was still there, it sat on the shelf and looked back at me. A Christmas movie in the middle of the year.

I approached the checkout counter, clutching the movie in my hand. Only to meet the long line of customers waiting to check out. As I stood in line, I absently glanced around the store. There was a jewelry case up in front, holding "valuable stock." I noticed something that resembled a large briefcase in the bottom. It was probably a sewing machine. With the checkout line moving at a snail's pace, my eyes explored other places around the store, but I kept going back to the jewelry case.

Could the briefcase actually be something from my thrift list? I looked behind me. The line had grown since I'd gotten in. I looked back up to the briefcase. If I didn't try, I would never know. If it was actually what I thought it was, I'd take it as another sign from Dad. I got out of line. The four-hundred-pound woman in the muumuu behind me claimed the vacant place as her own. I went to the counter and asked the clerk to open the case. He fumbled for the keys and opened the jewelry case.

"What do you want to see?"

"That brown case right there, please."

"'Kay." The clerk lifted the brown plastic case out with a little effort. "Here ya go."

"Thank you."

I took a breath and hesitated. I opened the clasps on the top of the case and lifted the handle to reveal a white JCPenney electric typewriter.

The midcentury modern electric typewriter was at the top of my list. I heard Dad's voice. "Will this work for you?"

I started crying from behind the grin on my face. "It's perfect."

I lugged the typewriter off the counter and got in line to check out. It was a "portable" for its time. The weight of the case alone was probably more than the MacBook Air I had in college.

Chapter 17

Depart

2014

I walked in the front door of Carla's house after coming from my future apartment. She was sitting in the living room. Mom was there too. They were chatting and seemed like they were actually getting along. I thought it looked like a good time to update them. I sat down on the couch across from Carla and Mom.

Carla asked, "What have you been up to this morning?"

"Well, guys, you know that guy from work that gave me a ride yesterday?"

"Yeah," Mom replied with caution.

"He took me up to his apartment yesterday." I could see Mom's eyes widen as she heard my words in a frightening context.

"Yeah," Mom said again, about to get sick.

"No, Mom. We're just friends."

"*Oh.* Cool." She let out with a sigh.

Carla looked over at her daughter and rolled her eyes. "Stacey. Come on. Let the boy talk."

"This morning, I went back and talked to a leasing agent. I found a place!"

"*Huh*?" they both replied.

"Aaahhh!" Carla came over and hugged me.

"When are you moving?" Carla asked.

"They have a space available, but I need to act quick. I'm moving out as soon as I can. There's just one hitch."

"You need a cosigner, right?" Carla beat me to the punch.

"I don't have bad credit. I just don't have credit. You can look at my financials. I will give you first and last month's rent as well." I desperately needed Carla to help. I showed her my bank statement.

"Well, I don't know where you learned to handle your finances like that, but good for you."

"So will you help me?" I eagerly asked.

"Go get in the car," Carla said

"Seriously?"

"Let's go before I change mind. Get in the car."

"Thank you!" I was elated. I had a path that I could walk down that would lead to a future. I could start a life.

We drove to the apartment complex. Carla and I went through the lease agreement with Sherri.

Sherri asked for my student ID. "If you are currently enrolled, you get a $150 credit on your account. You can use the extra savings to offset your books!"

I looked over at Carla and back at Sherri. "Uh, I haven't enrolled yet."

Sherri wanted to get me in as soon as possible. "Are you going to be enrolling this semester?"

"Yeah. I just need to go to the admissions office," I replied sheepishly

"Okay, cool! Just come in before the month ends and I'll put it onto your account."

"All right."

Carla looked at the lease agreement one more time and looked at me. "You are sure this is what you want?"

"Yes. I need to hit the ground running. I can't waste any more time."

"Okay," Carla said as she picked up the pen. "Don't screw it up. This is a good thing. You can do this." Carla signed the agreement and passed the pen to me.

"Thank you for doing this for me, Grandma," I said as I signed the agreement.

"This has to happen, Kameron. Just don't disappoint me. I'm going to miss you."

"I am going to miss you too, Grandma." We hugged and went to the car.

"So, school, huh?" Carla asked.

"Hit the ground running, right? I can take a few easy classes. The next semester is two months away. I'll have plenty of time to settle in."

"You sound like you've got it covered, Kameron. I have faith in you. You'll do just fine."

"Thanks. The biggest hurdle right now is moving into my new place."

2018
July 25, Wednesday, 9:00 a.m.

I woke up. Carla was still asleep. I had an opportunity to go through what I had left in my room at Carla's. As I approached the basement door, I paused.

This week was one of transition. Only two days had passed since I'd witnessed my father die. I needed to pronounce my past as deceased. I was terrified the next time I would visit that basement door could be for Carla's funeral. I exhaled and opened the door. When it swung open, I could see through to my room. Enough daylight peeked through the window wells that I didn't need to turn the light on.

I walked into my room. The oak bed, the desk, the plastic bin of odds and ends—all remnants of my childhood. All signs of the child I once was were reduced down to this. After Carla was gone, there would be no one, nothing, no identifiable sign of my existence in that house. I was fading. I threw out everything I could carry from my room. I needed to be erased on my own terms.

My room was now just "a room" in Carla's home. If I was going to truly be at home with the family I started with Kimmy, I had to move my mind and heart. Not just my stuff.

I grabbed my car keys. In a few days, I would bury my father. That day, I would bury myself, or at least the parts of me that needed to be.

I backed out of the driveway and pulled out of the cul-de-sac. Everything needed to go. I would soon go back to California. I wanted to truly go to California. I wanted to leave everything behind. I merged onto the 15 Freeway. I drove passed my mother's old apartment, the house that I concealed Mike Burton in.

I drove to Salt Lake. I parked in the garage next to the hotel. I was desperate to redo that night. Maybe Dad could have gotten over it if I didn't stop mike from killing himself.

I drove down the freeway. Instead of stopping at Carla's, I continued. When I got there, I drove down every street. They were the streets I grew up on. My school was there. My childhood home—the sidewalks where I learned to ride a bike, the lawn that once held a swing set. It wasn't empty. There were other children playing in the driveway. That was not my house. It was no longer my home. It was different.

The house was not waiting for me. It no longer knew me. We had parted ways long ago. I just didn't process it at the time. I let a breath out of my lungs, the air carried with it all the attachment I had weighing me down. My home was wherever my wife and children were. I'd chosen to uproot myself and replant those roots on my own terms. I promised myself that the only roots I would allow in my life would be good for me.

Chapter 18

Education

2014

September. A new month. A new life. A new home. Everything around me was new. For the first time in my life, I went to bed without telling anyone good night. I was the sole person aware of my location, my activities, and where I would go next. If I wanted to go anywhere, I didn't have to alert anyone, let alone ask for approval. I was the captain of my ship. The sheer freedom was exhilarating.

I was free. I went to all the restaurants I wanted to. If I wanted to cook something three times in a week I could. I brought my forty-inch TV with me from my room at Carla's place. For the first time, I spent solid weekends on PlayStation. When I got home from work, I watched entire seasons of my favorite television show in one day. I only stopped for restroom breaks and to restock my levels of soda and chips. Life was exactly how I wanted it. I lived on my terms.

I built my savings. Soon, I would have enough money to buy her—my dream car. I'd even named her. If anyone purchased the car before I had a chance to, I'd be heartbroken. At Quality Autohaus Automotive, she sat in the corner of the lot. Alisha was neglected but available.

A white 2003 BMW 325i was parked with two stickers on the windshield. One sticker claimed that the BMW had low miles. The other sticker said for $4,500 the black BMW could be mine. I had $2,700 in savings. I knew I could easily save the $1,800 I needed for the car by the time that I got my license. Both at night and during the day, I dreamed of going straight to the dealership from the DMV to pay cash for Alisha.

I felt at the time that I already had freedom. If I thought I was free as rode my bicycle passed Alisha on my way to and from work, the BMW would be the equivalent of a spaceship to me.

I continued to make the rounds. I went to work. I went home. I ate. I slept. I went to work again. What once manifested as freedom now was a routine.

2018
July 26, Thursday, 9:00 a.m.

Cremation was a reality. Every time the subject came up, I could see it in their eyes. It was as if my dad's family didn't feel like they would get Dad back if he was cremated; they wouldn't be able to lay him to rest properly.

I saw things a bit differently. Dad wasn't able to come back to this life. He wouldn't be able to evade death. Whether we put his remains in a large box or a small can, we would have to adjust to life without him.

My grandparents and aunts never met the Mike Burton that I had the displeasure of knowing. Little did they know they were about to walk into a minefield. I knew where almost every incendiary charge was planted. Mike was dangerous. But I was familiar with him. I had spent over nine months learning his layout. I could walk over Mike Burton in the dark without losing a toe. I knew where his tripwires were strung. I could disarm every charge Mike Burton had in his arsenal. His narcissism would be his downfall.

Mike burton was a scourge upon my father and plagued Dad's soul. Before Mike Burton entered the picture, Dad was the way we wanted him to remain in our minds.

Mike Burton was a man of compromising. He was in the driver's seat legally. Mike was driving our car with reckless abandon.

I knew if the Parkins pissed him off to a certain point, Mike would shut down and cease negotiation entirely. I had to intervene before war broke out. It's hard to split a body. It's harder to give everybody what they want. I relied on the hope that my family would eventually see what would happen as a good thing.

I called him.

"Hello?" Mike asked.

"Hey, Mike. Can you talk for a sec?"

"Sure, sonny! What is up?"

"So I just wanted to talk a little about final arrangements."

"Yeah, what's up? Are you okay with everything?"

"Yeah. You're saying Dad wanted to be cremated. I don't have a huge problem with that or anything. I think we should respect his wishes, but a lot of people are really not taking it very well."

"Well, it's not up to them. This is what Michael wanted, so we're going to do it. I don't like it either, but it's what he wanted, so we're going to do it. There's no questioning it, he told me that he wanted to be cremated."

"I talked to him a lot about death when I was having seizures. I even talked about what my funeral will look like and who would go. What would happen, et cetera. And I remember him saying,

> You know, Kameron, funerals are not really for the dead, they're for the living. I think funerals are to help people deal with the loss. When I am dead and gone, I want to be buried next to my grandma. I really don't care about the casket or the flowers. Whatever the family wants—that's what you should do.

"Mike, I feel like we're having a lot of tension and I'm thinking there's a better way that everybody can be happy, even Dad. We can give him what he wanted, and still ease the pain for everybody."

"Kameron, someone somewhere is going to not be happy with how this turns out. Everybody is unhappy to a large degree that this is happening at all."

"Yeah. I know. This fucking sucks. But what if there were a way?"

"A way for what?"

"A way to honor Dad's wishes and still let everybody deal with the loss and mourn in the way that they want to—casket, funeral, and all."

"Okay, yeah, I'm listening."

"Dad wanted to be cremated, right?"

"Yes, that is what he told me."

"So have him cremated."

"But I thought that was what was causing all the problems."

"It's part of the problem. I think that this is an opportunity for compromise."

"Huh?"

"If cremation is nonnegotiable, then let's have him cremated."

"How is that a compromise?"

"Once he is cremated, we can split the ashes—you can keep half, and the other half will go to the Parkins. I do imagine that they will bury him in the family cemetery, but you have half to carry out his final wishes. Take him to Monterey or keep him with you. Whatever you feel is right, but this way everybody gets a little piece of what they want. Everyone. You, me, the rest of the family, and most importantly, Dad. It's not perfect, but then again, what is perfect?"

"Huh. I guess that would work. Yeah, your dad would not really like it, but I guess that's the best way for everyone to get at least a little something of what they want. But he does want to be cremated. He told me that. I also have it in writing."

"Okay, so I guess it's settled then."

"Yeah, I guess."

"Bye, Michael."

"Bye, buddy."

I knew what Mike would do. There was no way he would turn over the entirety to us. But at least this way we got part of Dad.

Chapter 19

The Beginning of the End

2006

I was eleven years old that summer. It was a season that brought more heat than I ever experienced. A white-hot secret was on the brink of causing my family to combust. I knew my family was going to fall apart before they knew it. It was only when I came to know the truth that I was removed from the situation.

I boarded the airplane with Aunt Michelle and her children, destined for Fort Worth, Texas. I turned my head. Behind me, I saw a man and a woman.

By sending his son to another state, the man gained leverage over his wife. A power play to keep her in check. A damning secret about him was now vulnerable.

He had to protect himself and his son. The truth could potentially erase his relationship with his son. The truth could also erase a lot of other important things. His career, inheritance, reputation, and future were all in the hands of his wife.

The woman was threatened by the upper hand of her husband. Her son was just taken from her and held hostage. The boy was collateral to make sure she did not reveal the truth about her husband, his father. After all, if she did anything, the boy was in her husband's hands.

Exposing the truth could potentially erase her from her son's life. She also faced losing her home, her reputation, her friends, and her future if she revealed her husband for what he was.

The man and woman looked back at me. I looked into my parents' eyes as they blatantly lied to me. I was going on a "little trip" with my aunt. They didn't know that I was fully aware of my existence as a pawn in their marriage. I was just a piece in a game. My first trip in an airplane was a 1,200-mile journey away from my family.

After three months away, I didn't know if I still had a family to come back to. I didn't know if I would ever see my friends at school again. I didn't know which half of my family I would lose in the aftermath. Not a single person knew that I had a clue about what was going on.

I was alone. Knowledge was power. Knowledge was safety. Knowledge was also isolation. Knowing everything meant that I was a threat to everything. It served me well to not reveal the true extent of my understanding.

During my summer with my aunt, I was sheltered as my family imploded, nearly 1,200 miles and two states away from me.

Saturday was the day that my paternal grandmother and grandfather would pick me up. I stood in the front yard and waited for my grandparents to bring me back to the fire. To the site where my family once stood. I wanted to see the smoldering foundation. I wanted to see the damage. I wanted to finally be in the same world as everyone around me.

I was weary from holding all the secrets and tension of a marriage. I waited, but nobody came. I waited for their truck or their SUV. Nothing came. Just as I was about to go inside, I saw something turn around the impossibly tight corner. When the profile of a bus came toward me, I disregarded it and started for the front door of my aunt's home. Then I heard it, an air horn.

Calling out from three blocks away down the street. It was as if it was asking for me. As it approached, I saw that it wasn't a bus. In fact, it was a bit bigger. Rumbling down the private road, was a forty-foot luxury motorhome. Far beyond the weight constraints of the humble pavement, a $200,000 Fleetwood Discovery motorhome paraded through the neighborhood and arrived at my aunt's home. With a forty-six-point turn, my grandfather coaxed the monstrosity onto the driveway.

Taking up the entirety of the driveway and a significant portion of the adjacent yard, the Parkins' new motorhome made port next to my aunt's residence. I was going to be a part of its maiden voyage. It had seemed apparent that my mother had indeed revealed the family secrets. They had just blown almost a quarter of a million dollars on a land yacht. So much for my father's inheritance.

Now, the Parkins could live exactly as they wanted to. If they had to leave town, they could take their home with them. The motorhome was the perfect vehicle for them. A mobile safe room facilitating a self-sufficient state of denial. No longer did they need to compromise the comforts of home in order to evade the taxing family issues at their front door. They could sail away from their problems effectively in a ship that would weather through end times.

Grandma and Grandpa didn't know that I was aware of the predicament with Dad. They didn't know that I was more than collateral against Mom. They didn't know I knew the family secret that could burn the empire to the ground. I would be ready for whatever the future brought. When I returned to my home, Mom and Dad were at a stalemate.

2018
July 26, Thursday, 10:00 a.m.

I drove to the airport. Kimmy needed to come after all. I was almost at my breaking point. I knew I needed her to keep me level. I was afraid of what I would do without her at my side. I also knew her presence would make things more difficult.

I worked to stifle the part of me that Kimmy didn't know she married—the part of me that I enlisted to destroy Mike Burton. Less than forty-eight hours before, I chose to let a man live that I truly hated. In order to make that choice, my mind also had to host the concept of killing him. I wasn't sure what that said about my character.

I saw murder as an unfathomable act. However, in a small a portion of me, Mike Burton had expanded my horizons. He left me to navigate the seas, only after destroying my moral compass. I contemplated the irony. Mike Burton was the sole person that I ever felt homicidal about. Had I never met him, I might not have turned into a person capable of experiencing that emotion.

Once again, I began a balancing act. I could only be Dr. Jekyll around Kimmy. I concealed Mr. Hyde—he had to take care of Mike Burton, but I knew that Hyde would scare off my wife, possibly doing damage to our marriage. I would be damned if I let that happen. I had come too far and built myself up too high to let the evil tear me down. I resolved once again that after Mike Burton was out of our lives, Mr. Hyde would go down with him.

Kimmy and Lizzie stood holding hands next to the pickup lane at the airport. I pulled up and got out of the car, engine still running. They came up to me and hugged me. I sucked their support in like oxygen. I was close to drowning. After their embrace, I realized just how little air I had left.

Chapter 20

Oversteer

2009

Forty years prior to that day, my mother was born. That year on Mom's birthday, we moved into Grandma and Grandpa Parkin's house. The prospect of living there was strange but familiar.

Like camping in a backyard—living at their house was doable, but it wasn't a sustainable lifestyle. Who would choose to live outside, vulnerable, and open to threats when a perfectly safe shelter was just a few steps away? Mom, Dad, and I had a problem. We didn't have a home to retreat to anymore.

Moving into Grandma and Grandpa Parkin's house wasn't a choice. Mom and Dad were in a state of transition. I didn't know how long the marriage would last. They'd been on a downward spiral for upward of three years. I didn't know what would happen. But I knew my grandparents.

The five of us had one thing in common. We all knew of an unspoken truth residing, atomized, in the air. Our living situation was awkward. Grandma and Grandpa had been empty nesters for more than a decade. I knew that my grandparents enjoyed their space. They loved their family, but Grandma and Grandpa had indeed stretched out and gotten used to the empty space left behind after their children moved out.

Though it wasn't a small house, it erred on the side of cramped. Mom and Dad had the basement of the brown brick three-bedroom, two-bathroom house. I got the bedroom immediately across the hallway from Grandma and Grandpa. The nest was anything but empty, with us living there.

My first year of high school came and went. I had the luxury of being away from the youth of Juab County for long enough that my social record had been wiped. I was a stranger in the school. But I was also a native. I'd gone to kindergarten with the entire freshmen class. I knew everyone, though they had largely forgotten who I was. Only my name was familiar. Though my classmates didn't have a grasp of who I was, I remembered everyone. I knew the jocks, the cheerleaders, the nerds, the drama geeks—I had the upper hand.

We had trouble navigating the stress of cabin fever. Dad went to work every day. Mom was living in a place she never thought she would return to again. Grandpa and Grandma had given up their nest. They coped with the turmoil by engaging in one of their favorite pastimes—driving.

Grandma and Grandpa would drive through the small hometown, though they knew it like the back of their hand. My grandparents would examine every pore, look at every fine hair, every wrinkle—to check for any abnormalities in the beloved city. Grandma and Grandpa would cruise down the lanes of Nephi in their red F-150. Sipping ice-cold Coca-Cola, letting legal addictive stimulants carry them through the drive, as they admired the hometown that was as much a part of them as a limb. That summer, the Parkins had a passenger—me.

I would go along for the ride and survey the town with them. I was born there too. It was my home as well. Though I hadn't built quite the level of sentimentality they sustained for the place, I was heavily motivated to attend the outings by the prospect of a free soda.

The town was quaint, but I thought the people inside the cab of the truck were more deserving of my attention. I watched Grandma and Grandpa. I studied them. They were in somewhat of a pickle, socially, as they no longer had their house to themselves. They couldn't stay on the road forever. It was interesting to see that after so many years of marriage, Grandma and Grandpa held it together as well as they did.

That day, when Grandpa wanted to go on a drive. Grandma stayed home. It was just me and Grandpa. We took the other car that day. I thought the green Ford Explorer had a timeless look to it. Boxy yet subtle and smooth body lines. After getting our habitual "refreshing beverages," Grandpa took us to a place that was not included in the usual touring route of the town.

We made our way toward the Nephi Municipal Airport. Grandpa hadn't frequented it since he got rid of his airplane in the nineties. After pulling onto an abandoned runway, Grandpa shifted into neutral and coasted to a stop.

When he put the Explorer into park, he exited the car leaving the engine idling. He walked around the car. Before an explanation came to mind, I saw him just standing on the tarmac, as if waiting for someone or something to happen. Confused, I got out of the car and followed him.

When I reached Grandpa, he just looked at me, without any discernible facial expression whatsoever. Grandpa Parkin was as neutral and parked as the car. After a moment, Grandpa walked back to the car with his hands interlaced casually behind his back. Before I caught up to him, Grandpa Parkin had already gotten in on the passenger side. He waited, not looking directly at me. He just looked out toward the vacant, hazard-free asphalt. Though I didn't quite understand why, I didn't dare question him.

As I got behind the wheel, Grandpa asked, "You know which pedal is which, right?"

With as much of a confident façade as I could build, I replied. "Uh-huh."

"Good. Foot down hard on the brake. Shift into drive. Let off slow."

"Okay."

Though I only reached a speed of fifteen miles per hour in the airport, I'd barely tapped the accelerator. The power that I knew I had under my feet was exhilarating. We spent a half hour driving around the airport. After he had enough confidence that I wouldn't get us killed, Grandpa took it up a notch.

"Pull out there. We'll go on a little tour of West Nephi."

Grandpa was letting me go out onto a real street. Sure, it was used maybe once a day by a farmer, but it was a real road, with opposing traffic and intersections. The possibility of another car being on the road was intimidating, but for some reason, Grandpa had enough faith in me to let me do it. That was enough to keep me centered on the road. Grandpa wouldn't do something he wasn't sure of. If he thought I was ready to drive on a road, I knew that I must be able to. Though he seemed very lucid, I knew that early-onset dementia could happen to anyone.

We both saw an old farm truck come up the road.

"If anyone asks, you are fifteen and a half. Got it?" Grandpa said jokingly.

"Yeah, got it." I was trying to focus on the truck.

"Okay, relax. This is what people do on roads. It's what they are made for. Just keep a steady speed and stay straight. Be casual. Let him pass. There is more than enough road for both of you to get where you're going. You just stay on your side. Got it?"

"Yeah."

The old Dodge passed in a fleeting moment. Though it was a rush, it didn't feel as intimidating as I expected it would.

"Okay. Good. You've been on the road with other people. You're doing just fine Kameron."

"Uh-huh." I felt invincible.

In six months, Grandpa Parkin taught me about independence. Though I was given lessons about driving, I learned more about *navigating*. Sometimes, to make progress, one has to be outside the limits of society, in the fields. On the winding canyon roads less traveled. Mistakes weren't something that most people understood. The prospect of turning into a ditch doesn't have value to most people—but I didn't want to learn how to get out on my own. I had Grandpa Parkin to teach me. He put me in a ditch to learn how to drive back to the road. The key was applying power in the right amount. If I slammed the accelerator, we spun the wheels. If I let the engine do the work, the transmission would work with the wheels. Everything in the car needed to work together when it got stuck in order to get out.

Grandpa never made me crash the car. But he taught me how to turn into the slide—to use the potential for a crash to push through any danger. If something made my car turn the wrong direction Grandpa told me I would certainly roll if I turned *with* it.

The only way to avoid a fatal accident was to drive against the momentum. If I let myself get distracted by fear, losing control of the car would allow the momentum to end me. But focusing on what the car is doing, tuning out fear, I could use the momentum as a tool to regain control and end the problem. To use the weight of my car against itself—it would stabilize. I'd be able to correct it.

By the end of the year, I knew not to brake on ice. The car just needs to pass over it. Avoid abrupt movements. I needed to find my center of gravity before it found me. His rules of the road kept all four of my wheels down. Never accelerate before turning, or the wheel will be harder to turn. To brake for the corner. Stop hard, if I'm at high speed, then let out of the brake as I take the corner. Once a straight path comes, accelerate with caution and confidence. Always know my shoulders. Know who or what is behind me, next to me, and in front of me.

As Grandpa Parkin bestowed his experience on me from the passenger seat, I couldn't help but notice he seemed to be content there—teaching me, preparing me.

Nobody wanted to see the corner coming. Everyone knew we were going too fast. Our center of gravity was very high. Our road was covered with black ice and snow on the shoulders. At least for Grandpa Parkin and me, in those driving lessons, we found the brake.

2018
July 26, Thursday, 12:00 p.m.

There she was, at Carla's front door. I still didn't know how to interact with Mom. Almost every facet of our relationship was flawed. I didn't know if she trusted me. I knew I burned her. She had also burned me. We had crossed the bridge into and out of hell together. We both had fallen off that bridge several times. We pulled each other back to safety, only to be kicked off again into the fire. My relationship with my mother could be described by many words—due to it being in an ever-evolving state. One day we could be perfectly normal and talking about any subject, perfectly casual. The next day, I would hear the subtle slur in her voice and know.

I didn't know how to proceed. Both of my parents let go of me before I was ready. I fell into the river of life, not knowing how to swim. I'd spent the last ten years of my life gasping for air. Watching from below the surface. I drifted farther as they stood still. My father—consumed by Mike Burton. My mother—consumed by a desperate search for a way to cope. Something clicked in me early on. I didn't want to drown.

I didn't want to rely on the possibility of my parents diving in after me. If I did wait for them, I knew I wouldn't have enough breath to get to safety on my own. Whenever I made an effort to look for them, the distance only grew. The only option I had was to figure out how to swim. By the time I reached the surface, I was too far to be heard. I yelled, but they couldn't hear me. Mike Burton was always louder.

I didn't know if my mother was better. I didn't know if she could "dive in" after me. I never really knew if she forgave me for what I did to her. I also didn't know if I'd forgiven her for what she put me through. However, I did know one thing to be true. My dad was lost. I only had one parent left on the riverside.

Chapter 21

Finding the Missing Piece

2014

December. All I saw around me was happiness. But I wasn't happy. I was the opposite of happy. The solitude was debilitating. I had survivor's guilt from my own life. I was supposed to die. Now I wasn't dying. Most people don't get mad at God for a cure to a disease. I wasn't most people.

I mourned my own death. There was no one to blame. It was just reality. Soon, I'd figure out what was on the other side. Now, I had a future to deal with.

Right after the surgery, I was elated. I was motivated to make my second chance worth it. For some reason, I was supposed to be here. I had something to do on this earth, and I was meant for something great. After a few months, my demeanor became less enthusiastic.

I feared the unknown. I was back at square one. I was in the same place that I was a year before when I was told that I had no future. Except this time, I had time. I had variability. I lost predictability. Every day I spent alone was a day that I had to spend with myself. I had always been alone with my thoughts. This time, neither one of us knew what to do with the seemingly infinite avenues to choose from. I needed an escape.

I knew that my old vice would numb me as effectively as the alcohol my father used. The demon was old. I hadn't visited it for years. But it was a demon, nonetheless. I stayed away from alcohol, cigarettes, and drugs. I found an escape in my youth that was much easier to conceal, with far fewer side effects.

I was in a new place. I had moved out; I was on my own. I had complete autonomy. I did not have to answer to anyone. I went to Craigslist and found the NSA section. Within an hour, I was on the train up to Salt Lake to hook up with a girl named Nina.

The train stopped; I could see the Motel 6 sign in the distance. I started walking down the cabin to the exit. When I stepped onto the yellow nonslip tiles of the platform, I felt a hand on my shoulder. I knew that hand. I last felt it eleven months before. It was the last time I felt Joe's hand before he died.

I heard his voice. "Kameron, don't do this. What are you thinking, boy? You know that once you start this, you won't be able to come back from it. Do it the right way. Not like this."

I fell to the ground. I was astonished at what just happened. I looked back up into the distance. The Motel 6 sign was enticing me to come and have a meaningless one night stand, to screw my depression away. I walked back to the platform. The next southbound train was fifty-three minutes away. I sat on the bench and waited on the deserted platform for a train to take me home. I got home at 2:00 a.m. I walked through the door of my apartment and into my bedroom. Luckily my roommate was once again partying elsewhere.

I fell to my knees and prayed—sort of. "Okay, God. Fuck it. We'll do it your way. I can't be alone. You know it. I know it. But if we are gonna do this, I need your help. I can't go through all the dating shit. I need you to bring her to me. I am so tired. I don't know what to look for or how to find it. I just need the right woman. The one who I need to be with. I just want someone to hold at night. Give me that, and I will do whatever you want. I just don't have much time."

Two and a half weeks later. I came home from school. My other roommate was at the apartment. He was not alone. Standing in the apartment, his date was waiting for him to grab some things for a party they were headed to. At a glance, she was attractive enough.

My first thought was maybe I was meant to steal her away from my roommate. That would be extremely easy. He was such a dimwit that it was hard for me to even comprehend that he was capable of bringing a date back to the apartment. While he was getting ready, we started talking. Almost immediately I knew she was not, in fact, "the one."

She began. "Hey. What's your name?"

"I'm Kameron. You?"

"I'm Danielle."

"Hi, Danielle."

Immediately, she inquired, "Hey, are you by chance single?"

Puzzled, I responded, "Uh, yeah. You already have a date though. Why do you ask?"

She looked at my left hand. "You have a messed-up hand. Has it always been like that? My friend has a screwed-up hand like yours. Except it's the other side, I think. She is single. I could set you up if you want!"

Sarcastically, I replied, "*Oh*, that is so cool! I have been waiting for someone like that! I am sure we would make a great couple! We could make one whole set of hands!"

With the humor going right over her head, she was overjoyed. "I *know*! Oh my gosh, Kimmy is gonna flip! Here, I'll send her a photo of you!"

I was annoyed. I was also fearful of the high amount of energy packed into the tiny woman. I decided to humor her. Feeling like I was on a nature special featuring the two last animals of a species, I agreed to let Danielle send her roommate a photo of me.

I saw the text. It read, "What do you think?"

"Yeah. Who is he?"

"YOUR DATE!"

"What? Dani, come on."

"Well, do you think he is cute?"

"Yeah. But."

"BUT WHAT? YOU GUYS ARE GOING OUT. I'M SETTING YOU UP."

"Whatever."

"So does she actually want to be set up?" I asked.

"Yeah, totally!" She was lying through her teeth.

"Cool, when are we doing this?" I was less than optimistic.

Dani replied, "Here is her number. You guys work it out."

She wrote Kimmy's number down on the back of my English notebook. I was getting a bit nervous. I may have bitten off more than I could chew.

Dani handed me the notebook and chirped. "You're *welcome*!"

My poor roommate came out of his bedroom, and they left the apartment. I figured I might as well try it. I composed a new text message addressed to the woman that my matchmaker picked out for me.

"Hello, my name is Kameron—I think your, uh, friend is trying to set us up. Are you Kimmy?"

"Yeah. Sorry. She can be a bit too much sometimes. Don't worry about it."

"Well, do you not want to go out? Because this Dani Chick seems to know her stuff. We just might be soulmates! Lol :)."

"HAHA."

"I totally get it if you don't want to go out. Personally, I'm kind of scared of her. I'm not sure what she will do if we don't. She knows where I live. You would kinda be helping me out if we went on one date. Then you can tell her I'm a loser."

"What if you are a loser?"

"I don't wanna die! Has Dani ever been in prison?"

"Maybe. She doesn't talk about it."

"I get it. Lock up hardens people. I still think she might hurt me. One date? I'll be nice to you. I have a feeling Dani will shiv me prison-style if I'm not good…"

"ROTFL! Okay. one date."

"Awesome! Where do you want to go?"

"Danielle just texted me and thinks it's safer to go on a group date."

"Kimmy, are you a predator?"

"Ha ha. No, are you?"

"Would we tell each other if we were?"

"Good point."

"Well, Kameron, the not predator, we are thinking sushi. You like sushi?"

"Sushi is great!"

"Yeah, there is a place called Sushi Ya. it's on State Street and Sixteenth Street. You know it?"

"Yeah! Sounds great!"

"This Friday night, four o'clock?"

"Perfect," I said. If this connection went anywhere, it would be a relationship born in a lie. It was a Tuesday afternoon. I had three days to figure out what sushi was and to figure out if I liked it or not.

I met Kimmy at her apartment. Unbeknownst to me, the plan for the evening changed. Kimmy and I would be joined by Danielle and another roommate. My roommate had bailed on the night. I felt like I was going to my own trial.

I was greeted by Danielle at the door. She invited me in and presented Kimmy and me to each other. Excitedly, Dani pushed us together as if she was trying to get two prized dogs to mate. I decided to roll with it and enthusiastically approached my date.

When I went up and hugged her, I did it as a joke, Dani was over the moon due to the interaction. But I noticed that Kimmy didn't pull away. I thought that was interesting. Maybe there was some chemistry, after all. I backed up and put my new prospect into full view. When I saw Kimmy, I didn't quite know how to define her.

There was a lot more to Kimmy than the headshot Danielle provided me. I could tell that her disability was much worse than mine. She walked with a considerable limp. I could see her affected side, which was the opposite of mine, was far less developed and weaker. Her eyes were perfect. Her smile was contagious. And her laugh was absolutely identifiable—a dead ringer for Ernie from Sesame Street. She wasn't pretty in the world's definition of beauty. However, there was something about her. Inside her that exuded something beautiful.

Dani chauffeured us to my character evaluation. We rode to the sushi bar in her '90-something Toyota Camry. The vehicle was a rolling death trap. The peeling purple paint of the body and the mismatched door panels were the least of its problems. The steering wheel was removed for repair at some point in the past. When the technician replaced the wheel, he installed it upside down. Who knew what would happen if the airbag deployed.

We arrived at the sushi bar. Thankfully we were just as alive as the koi fish swimming around the porcelain Buddha in the pond. I wracked my brain for a reason to take the bus home. I also was trying to figure out how to not ask the girl out on a second date. How do you not do a second date with someone like her and make it a convincing reason? Also, how does one eat raw fish? I had a lot on my mind.

Danielle and Tori got their own table. They left us alone so we could get to know each other. Danielle waved her hand and proudly walked off. "See you two love birds later."

Kimmy apologized for Dani. "Sorry. She has two speeds. Annoying and asleep."

"It'd be interesting to see her sleepwalk," I replied. We sat down and ordered. I found the least intimidating thing on the menu. "I will take a California roll to start and iced water." I thought I could stomach crab, cucumber, and avocado.

Kimmy ordered, "I will have a dragon, an Alaska, and a shrimp tempura roll."

I saw that Kimmy definitely knew what she wanted. "Sushi is much cheaper if you don't order by the roll, check the option and it's the same price as one roll," she explained.

"Oh," I said. I was hoping she wasn't onto my lack of experience with sushi. The first round came. I decided to dive in. It was amazing. I just acquired a new favorite food. I desperately hoped I could keep it down.

I was much more adventurous with the next round. I was also adventurous with the conversation.

We went through the standard small talk and questions that two people engage in on a first date. The more we talked, the more I sat and looked at her. She was definitely not what I had in my mind when I pictured a mate. But with every slice of raw fish, slices of my mental model of perfection fell away.

I was mesmerized by her smile. Her eyes. Her Ernie-esque laughter. I walked into the date knowing that I would have to cut her loose at some point. And it had to be quick. I didn't want to string her along and be cruel.

It would be mean to lead on someone like her, who hadn't had many dates. I didn't want her to get her hopes up. I didn't want to hurt her. Maybe, just maybe, I could ask her on one more date before jumping ship.

We left the bar, filled to the brim with raw fish and rice. My wallet was much lighter too. I learned that such a good meal costs over $35 per person. I guess I should have researched that.

We climbed back into the death trap and went back to her apartment complex. I walked Kimmy to her door. My tongue went back and forth behind my bottom teeth. I knew that I could get her to go out on a second date. Still, I didn't know what the exit strategy would be. I wanted more time with her, but how would I get out? I still had plenty of time to work on that problem.

I took in a breath. "So how 'bout that second date we talked about? You wanna get together next week?"

She smiled. "Uh, sure!"

Eagerly I suggested, "What about Wednesday night?" I couldn't wait another week to see her.

"Sounds fine!" Kimmy replied.

"Great, see you then." I wanted to take her answer and run. I walked down the breezeway, and as soon as I was out of sight, I started skipping. I was elated. I didn't know why. After all, the plan was to end the fling after the next date. Or maybe a few. Three wouldn't get anyone's hopes up, right? I got home and waited out the long weekend.

Wednesday finally came. I ditched school. Cleaning a student apartment from top to bottom took an entire day. I didn't have any money left to take Kimmy out anywhere, thanks to the sushi date. I decided to embrace my romantic side (as well as my cheap and inventive side). That night I would cook for Kimmy in my apartment, and we would watch a movie. *The Notebook*. What chick doesn't love *The Notebook*, right?

I picked her up and brought her back to my apartment. An awkward apartment tour and a terribly overcooked Italian meal later, we were sitting on the sofa watching one of the most depressing chick flicks in my movie library.

Our first kiss was in the style of young children in a schoolyard. It was quaint. From the kiss, I could definitely tell that she had zero experience with the act. Hell, honestly, I was a novice too. So I said, "Mmm. That was kinda average. Let's try again." It was better. Electric. Not high voltage. But definitely powerful enough for me to notice a current.

I didn't know what was happening. This was designed to fail. And now I was kissing her? What was I doing? Suddenly we heard the doorknob rattle. My roommate came into the apartment with Danielle. Dani brought along a few friends too. The date was definitely over. After the movie ended, we all got up from the now very full couch. As everyone was leaving, I took Kimmy aside and asked her out on a third date. To my relief, she was in favor of the idea. I really hoped she survived the ride home in Dani's Camry.

I lay in my bed that night wondering why I asked Kimmy out on yet another date. Why was I not cutting her loose? Why did I kiss her? Why did I want to kiss her again? What was going on with me? Before long, Kimmy was all I could think about. Everything I experienced was processed through the lens of how Kimmy would react.

I felt like I was lost, like I was losing my autonomy. The weirdest part of it all was I liked it.

The day of the third date came. I picked her up, and we went to Applebee's. Luckily payday was the day before, and I didn't have to inflict my cooking skills on Kimmy again. We sat at the table and endured the laggard service. As we were talking, my eyes panned out and I just looked at her.

It hit me like the public transit bus that I had been using as my forty-foot chariot to chauffeur Kimmy around. The woman across the table from me was absolutely stunning. She was perfect. I didn't know why it hadn't occurred to me sooner. I felt really stupid and regretted all the time that I worried about an exit strategy.

Kimmy, in the world's eyes, was broken. Incomplete, damaged, disabled, limited. She was never going to be equivalent to a person without cerebral palsy. Society defined her as less than whole. I was on a mission. I was looking for a mate. I desperately wanted to find the one.

I did not want to date around and search through a haystack for her. I wanted someone beautiful. I wanted society's definition of the perfect woman.

I never realized that I was incomplete. I never considered myself damaged, disabled, or limited. I did feel less than whole, but I couldn't figure out why. I was just depressed. That was my label—depressed. At that moment, it clicked. With her smile and the look of innocence in her eyes, I realized that I was a very stupid man. I was searching my whole life for the wrong thing. I wanted the world's definition of beauty. But what would repair me was something I never actually searched for and much harder to find.

I needed the perfect woman for me.

Kimmy had all the missing pieces. My left hand didn't work. Kimmy's did. My right leg was as strong as an ox; her leg dragged on the ground. Physically speaking, we literally made one completely functional person between our disabilities. But more importantly to me, her soul was as light as mine was dark.

Kimmy and I were the perfect match for each other. Kimmy was my equilibrium. We were three dates into the relationship. I knew what I had to do. I knew my exit strategy. Kimmy was my exit strategy from myself.

As if I hadn't had enough confirmation from the universe, when I dropped her off at her apartment, I met her fourth roommate for the first time.

Asha was a very attractive woman whom I would be very much attracted to, had I not met Kimmy. She was a full-time student, a ballroom dance major. She kept long hours because she had to pay her own way through school.

One of her part-time jobs happened to be at a jewelry store. When she wasn't at school or with her boyfriend, Asha sold and cleaned engagement rings.

2018
July 27, Friday, 2:00 p.m.

I knocked three times. The house was hauntingly similar to the one I lived in as a child. The yard was on the smaller side, but the lawn was manicured. While waiting to be let in, I took a step back and admired the home. I used to live in a home like this one. My parents used to have the best house in the family. We used to be the ones who entertained. We were the ones who had the barbeques, hosted the holiday parties, the family get-togethers—but that was before things fell apart. That was a lifetime ago.

Josh, my little cousin, opened the door. "Hi, Kameron."

"Hey, Josh." He wasn't so little anymore. The mental snapshot I had of him was frozen at six years old. Now Josh was sixteen. He was taller than me. Josh wasn't little at all.

"Everyone is in the dining room."

"Cool, thanks." Not everyone, I thought. I walked through the door and into the foyer of Michelle's house. I looked through to the back of the house and saw them at the dining room table.

I walked through the living room, the staircase, passed the kitchen, and found myself standing in Michelle's dining room. It was humbly furnished, but the square footage was something to be coveted. In a different universe, I might have been standing in my parents' house.

There they were. Katie, Michelle, Michelle's husband (Todd), and my grandparents. I saw them just a month before at a BBQ. They huddled around a mountain of photo albums grinding the gears of their emotional transmission, shifting between laughing, crying, chuckling, sobbing. Never fully in one display of emotion. It was a turbulent mix of emotion that they were all trying to get through together.

Grandpa got up and hugged me. "Glad you came, Kameron."

"Me too. So what are we doing?"

Michelle motioned to a chair at the end of the table, "Come look, we are putting together a slideshow for the memorial. Going through a ton of pictures."

"Cool." On the table, half a dozen photo albums lay open. We had less than twenty-four hours to put together a compilation that would represent all the highlights in Dad's life. Childhood photos, photos of dad as a missionary, photos from college, an album of his early days as a father, as a husband—the Michael Parkin that we were hoping to remember appeared to still be intact. There was still a substantial part of him that was left unscathed by Mike Burton.

I sat down and tried to insert myself in the process. They were scouring each album, Todd was in the living room at his computer, scanning stacks of photos and arranging them.

It was difficult to see his sisters and parents process each photo. It was more difficult to see what wasn't there. Just last month, I had sat in the same chair and looked across the same table at my father. Now I looked across the table, and his chair was empty. Instead of planning a routine barbeque, we were planning a funeral. It didn't seem real.

Everyone was lost in their own recollection of Dad. I wasn't. I looked around and saw the emotions that rolled through the room. As they tried to keep their boats from capsizing, waves beat them from both sides. I didn't know if I was hurting or helping the situation by being present. I was Dad's only child. But I was also an extension of him—a remnant.

When my father abandoned me, so did they. His family made no effort to hold onto a connection to me before when he left everyone for Mike Burton. They deemed me as a package deal with my father, in regard to a relationship with them. Now that he was gone for good, what use would they have for me?

When I saw my grandmother, I looked aside, out the window. I recalled a conversation I'd had with her in the past, when I was estranged from dad. The words we'd exchanged haunted me.

"Grandma, there are things between me and my dad that I can't fix because he won't work with me. But I still want you in my life. Are you capable of having me in your life even if I don't have a relationship with him?"

"Kameron, He is my son. I can't. Why can't you try harder to fix things with your father? I wish you would just quit and make things right with him."

When Grandma and I had that exchange, something changed. From then on, I could tell that Phyllis's ultimate loyalty was to her son, not to her family. He was her son. And I was her grandson. But it was apparent from her words that my title didn't mean much to her. I was chopped liver, as it were. There wasn't any reason that I could see for her to regard me as a good thing in her life if I came without her son. With Dad gone, she no longer had a choice. If she wanted me in her life, I would no longer come with my dad. My presence might very well be too much for her to handle.

Whether I liked it or not, from that moment, I was branded in the family by the death of my father. I was the only part of him that was still living. I didn't know if that was a good thing or a bad thing. I definitely understood that my role in the family had changed.

Chapter 22

Attachments

2015

The weekend passed. I would be skipping class that Monday. I knew the only time I could talk to Asha was when Kimmy and I were both in class. Monday morning came. I woke up and got ready for work. As I rode on my bike, I approached the car dealership where Alisha was parked. She still sat in the corner waiting. It appeared as if the car were watching me go by one last time. I knew I had something far more important to purchase than a secondhand BMW.

I got through what seemed like the longest Monday workday of my life. After work, I would go to the jewelry store where Kimmy's roommate worked and pick a stone that. If I played my cards right, Kimmy would wear on her finger for the rest of her life. A life shared with me. It was 2:11 p.m. I hung up my last phone call. I put my headset on the desk and grabbed my bag. It was time to run out the door. With keys in hand, I went for my bike lock. I mounted my bike and went straight to the jewelry store.

When I got there, I paused at the door. Once I walked in, I was committed, Asha would know what I was there for. I definitely wasn't there for anyone else. I trusted her enough to stay quiet. I pushed through the door. The electronic *ding* that the door made as

I entered summoned Asha from the back room. She was organizing stock. Asha recognized me right away.

"Oh, hey there! You lookin' for something in particular?" she asked in a very coy attitude.

I sheepishly replied with a "Maybe."

"I was wondering when I would see you come in here."

"Please don't out me," I pleaded.

"Why would I do that? It'd take all the fun out of it." Asha giggled with enthusiasm. She was having fun with the situation. Somehow, I didn't feel like this was the first time Asha played an anonymous role in a friend's engagement.

"I don't know. I'm just nervous."

"Don't be nervous," Asha said. "You could propose with a mood ring from the gas station and she would say yes to you. You and Kimmy are perfect together. I've seen the way she looks at you. You can do this. But I think we are fresh out of mood rings. Let's find something that is more...Kimmy."

"Okay, let's do this!" Asha was very encouraging. She was perfect for this job. It was also nice to have a woman's perspective that I trusted to help find just the ring.

"First, do you have an idea of where you would like to land, price-wise?"

"I'm paying cash. Don't show me anything over two thousand."

"All right. We have several options with that budget. You can get pretty much any setting, then we can figure out how much you want to spend on the stone. Sound good?"

"Yeah, sounds great!"

"Cool, go through the case and call for me if there are any rings you want to get a closer look at."

"Thanks, Asha!"

"Have fun, Kameron."

Asha went back to her counter and left me to browse. There were so many rings. Each one had a personality. They were distinctive. They made statements. They would all eventually be sold to people—people who had personalities that matched up with that of each ring in the case. Each ring was different. They all said different things. I Immediately saw a setting that caught my eye. I wanted to go with my gut. But I still felt like I had to examine every ring in the store. I put that ring aside while I kept searching. Every ring was off. None of them were right. None of them were Kimmy.

I got frustrated. The ring I'd set aside was waiting for me to make up my mind. I gave up looking. I returned back to the first ring that caught my eye. I didn't know why I set it aside, but the second time we met, the ring started talking to me. It was absolutely perfect. When I gave myself a chance to shut out the other rings in the store, it made even more sense why the ring was the one. I came to my conclusion about the ring in a way, not unlike the way I figured out my feelings about the woman it would belong to.

The white gold setting, a soft metal, was prone to scratching, but when polished, it looked as desirable as the day it was created. Stones on the ring were arranged in a peculiar fashion. When I looked closer, the setting was even more amazing.

The setting was a wedding set. It had an engagement ring. As well as a wedding band. Six smaller diamonds on the wedding band wrapped and upheld the main stone on the engagement ring. As if the smaller diamonds were carrying and showcasing the centerpiece, I knew that once Kimmy and I were married, the diamond moments would not cease; they would continue coming to support the first diamond—her.

I called for Asha.

"Hey, you find any you like?"

"I found the one. What's the price?" I pointed to the ring.

"It depends. We custom-build the rings. That setting is $1,100. You can go through each stone to make sure it's to your liking. I'll get Dave, the jeweler, out here to go through that part with you."

Dave came out to find me. "You Asha's friend?"

"Yeah, that's me."

"You've picked the setting, that's the easy part. Now we have the fun part to attend to—choosing the stones."

"Okay," I replied nervously.

Dave pointed to his office. "Follow me." Dave grabbed the ring from Asha before he went back to his office. "Asha said you have a budget, right?"

"Yeah. I would like to stick to two thousand dollars."

Dave, the jeweler, sat down at his desk and motioned for me to do the same. Dave examined the ring I'd chosen. "With this setting, we have just under a couple grand to work with.

"There are a lot of stones in that ring, how much is it right now?" I asked.

"Right now, the stones are CZ—fake. Just for show. But we can fix that." He spun away from his desk and sprang from his tan leather desk chair. Just then, I noticed the large safe in the corner that I'd passed by on my way into his office. It was the size of a standard refrigerator. He turned the dial just ever so slightly.

After turning a gold wheel, the heavy-duty door swung open for Dave. The big metal box wasn't just a safe; it was a treasure chest. Inside, dozens of black suede bags were stacked on top of each other. There were ring-sized boxes and bracelet-sized boxes. Rack after rack of rings. He leaned in on the safe with his right hand while he massaged his chin with his left, as though he was looking for something specific.

After a moment, Dave the jeweler reached for one of the small suede pouches. "Ah, yep. This'll work." He walked back to his desk with the pouch. On his desk sat a large tray made of the same material as the pouch in his hand. He untied the top and let the contents spill out into the tray.

"Wow. So those are diamonds?" I asked.

"Those are diamonds," Dave said as he reached for the tweezers in his shirt pocket.

I was starting to get nervous about how much this ring was going to end up costing. "So I can get seven stones for under two thousand?"

"I think we can make a ring out of what is in this bag. The good news is that stone prices are more complex than most people think." Dave positioned all the diamonds in lines on the suede tray.

"You can get a stone that is flawless and twice the price of another stone with similar qualities. And it will be less shiny. Likewise, you can get a stone with a minor flaw in it, but it will be a different price than a comparable stone because the rock has a tint to it."

"Let's pick the smaller stones first. They're easier. Then we will save the big one for last." Dave pulled another little tool out of his shirt pocket. "This is what we jewelers call a loop. It'll get you a closer look."

I took the loop. "How do I pick the best ones?" I didn't want to go over budget. But I also didn't want to get bad stones.

"These are all the best ones. With your budget, you can get a really decent ring. These smaller stones don't matter as much as the centerpiece, but I want you to have the chance to see each one."

"Okay." I picked out six diamonds.

Dave brought over another pouch. Inside were three stones. "This one is flawless, but it is a lower karat."

I looked at the stone while he got the next one out to show me.

"This second stone is interesting. It has a brown tint. In the right light, it looks like a different gem." Dave handed me the tweezers.

I examined the two stones. "What about that one."

There was a third diamond waiting. "This diamond is the most brilliant of the three. It refracts light very well. It also has a flaw. Most stones do have flaws. It is probably the most brilliant of the three."

"And the most expensive, I presume?"

"Yes. Of the three diamonds, that stone has the highest price."

"It's the brightest diamond despite its flaw?"

"Yes," Dave replied.

"With the least expensive stone, what am I looking at, price-wise?"

"With the six other gems you picked, that configuration would be around $1,950."

"And the second stone?"

"You are in the neighborhood of $2,200."

"The third one with the flaw?"

"$2,550."

"Dang it."

"What's wrong?"

"The third stone is perfect. It's flawed and perfect because of it. That stone is the stone. But it's outside of my price range. The ring is a perfect representation of the woman."

I knew that I had a bit more than $2,000. I could just save it again. I only got one shot at this. And, Kimmy, if she said yes, would be wearing this ring for the rest of her life. It had to be perfect.

I was hesitant.

"All right, I know that you are trying to win over one of Asha's friends. You said you are buying today, paying in full without financing?"

"Yes."

"If you pay the entire amount today, I will work with you on the price. You are trying to stay at $2,000, correct?"

"Yes." I became giddy inside, but I tried to control myself.

Dave pursed his lips as he looked down at the tray, still containing half a dozen diamonds. "$2,400 and it is yours."

"Ha! That'd be amazing! Let's do this!"

"Your ring will be ready to pick up later today."

"All right. I will see you later then. Thank you!"

I walked out of the store completely high. Part of me was elated. Part of me was nauseated. I couldn't believe what I was doing. I went home to plan. It had to be perfect. I would only get one shot.

2018
July 29, Sunday, 9:00 a.m.

That day would have been their twenty-fifth wedding anniversary. Mom had been worn down by dad, by Mike Burton, and by everything else. After I defined her as a simple addict for over ten years, I realized exactly why my mother was the way she was. Botched surgeries, having her moral character crucified by her family, a lifetime of disappointment, and having been a symbol of mistrust—Mom's pain was indeed real. It manifested in physiological form. She was truly weathered by her life. Yet sometimes she'd have a glimmer in her face of the person she was before the storm. The mother I knew from my early childhood.

I longed for just one thing from my mother. To go back. to somehow catch her in her positive state. To preserve and enjoy a relationship with the mother I knew, without the fear of losing her. Every time I saw her or spoke on the phone with Mom, I knew that she would inevitably slip through my fingers like dry sand. It wasn't that I didn't trust her. Mom's behavior was extremely dependable. I was depressed by her. My relationship with her was a hologram. For the longest time, I wondered if her mortality would soothe me. With many people, I saw death as a way to lessen the sadness of a failed relationship. But after my dad, my sadness wasn't quite lessened.

Along with my world view, my perspective of my mother shifted. She was battered and worn from her life. For all I knew, she didn't have much time either. Something had to change. I needed to let go of who I thought Mom was. If I gave her the chance to tell me, maybe I wouldn't make the mistake of cashing out too early.

Chapter 23

Engagement

2015

That day was the day. I had the ring, I knew what to do with it, but I had no clue how to go about it. I was 95 percent sure she would say yes, but I didn't know for sure. It was the first time that I had proposed to anyone, and I was nervous as hell. We had talked about it jokingly, but once I put this question out there, she would know my real intent. Did she actually want to get married? Did she think I was a good candidate? I knew she was the one for me, but I had no clue what was going on inside her head. Little did I know that I would seldom ever know the goings-on inside Kimmy Sherman's head.

I picked Kimmy up from her apartment. We were headed up to Salt Lake. I had a "doctor's appointment." I asked her if she wanted to go along with me so we could go on a date up in Salt Lake City afterward. I had the ring from the jewelry store in my pocket. I'd spent the last week practicing my draw. My pocket was not quite big enough to conceal the ring box. I had to come up with a plan to conceal the box for the entire day. I decided to wear a man purse. When Kimmy questioned my fashion accessory, I just said, "Eh. It has more flexibility than a wallet."

I still couldn't drive, so we took the train up to Salt Lake City. This had to work. She had to say yes. Otherwise, it would be a terribly awkward ride home. I was almost certain that she would say yes. She had to say yes. I needed her in my life. I didn't know when or how, but the universe just put her there. Right in front of me. And the crazy thing is, I asked for her. I hadn't even known her six months, and I knew that I could spend sixty years with her.

I held my man-purse on the train like I was preparing for the possibility of getting mugged. I poured the lion's share of my savings into the ring, in hopes that Kimmy would say yes. With one sweaty palm clutching my man bag, and the other squeezing Kimmy's hand, we both looked out the window of the train car as it rolled forward toward Salt Lake City.

The train arrived at Temple Square Station. I wanted to get the doctor's appointment over and done with as soon as possible, then proceed with my plan. I had a problem. I didn't have a plan. I thought playing it by ear was a good idea at the time—before I picked up Kimmy. But it just led to panic. I had no clue what or how I would do it, I just knew that it needed to work.

The doctor's appointment was relatively painless. We were in and out in under an hour. The light rail took us to Temple Square.

The Salt Lake Temple was the symbol of the church and the God that I was born believing in. It was the symbol that I once denounced, but now it would save me. When I broke down and asked God for someone, he gave me someone. It seemed only fitting to propose in his front yard. I just had to figure out a way to do it.

As we walked through the city, we played music—different songs on our playlists from our phones. For the most part, we had similar taste in music. It clicked. Earlier in the week, I'd gone through the different ways to do what I was about to do. Flash mobs were off the table. Kimmy didn't like a lot of attention drawn to her. But I did like the idea of proposing with music. Albeit without the crowd.

The perfect song came to mind. I cued "Love Story" by Taylor Swift. I took in a deep breath, praying that I wouldn't pass out, and asked her to dance.

We stood in front of a fountain. The music started playing. We were both familiar with the tune. I hoped that I could get through the whole thing before she realized what was going on. Unfortunately, the line that mentioned getting married was in the last verse, and if she figured it out, it would've been a really awkward dance to get out of, knowing that there is a proposal coming. As we stumbled through the dance, the third verse came.

"Is this in my head? I don't know what to think, he knelt to the ground and pulled out a ring and said, 'Marry me, Juliet, you'll never have to be alone. I love you and that's all I really know. I talked to your dad, go pick out a white dress, it's a love story, baby, just say yes."

We stopped dancing about halfway through the third verse. I was looking up at her, letting the music play. When she saw the ring, she didn't run. I thought that was a good sign.

Thankfully, Asha had covertly obtained her finger size. The ring was a perfect fit. I walked into that garden, thinking that I had a tentative maybe, but I walked out with a yes and a fiancée.

I had just one problem.

Introductions had to be made.

2018
July 30, Monday, 9:00 a.m.

We drove up the road leading to the chapel. I parked in the corner of the lot. Thirty minutes passed by before anyone else arrived. My right hand rested on the center console of the car. Kimmy took it. I didn't know what to feel that day. I knew funerals were for the living. I had made my peace with the situation. The chapel would soon be filled with people who loved or cared about my father.

Now was the time to grasp composure with an iron fist. No one wanted to see me lose it. So what was the point? If I was a support to other people, I would have a duty not to break. I supported. Grandma and Grandpa came down the road toward the church. Dad had always made fun of his father's snail-paced driving—that day was different. That day, his parents traveled down the road with a very somber cadence.

Their maroon Ford F-150 sparkled in the morning sunlight. Charles and Phyllis looked as if they were fighting the path. Maybe they would get just a few more moments before the memorial if they drove just a bit slower. As they approached, a third passenger became visible through the windshield. Dad's urn sat on the center console. His parents both rode with a hand on the urn. Whether seeking or providing comfort, the emotion in the cab nearly busted the doors of their truck off the hinges.

We got out of the car and went up to them. A peculiar aura blanketed the area. Everyone could communicate nonverbally. We were all experiencing the same emotions. We all were hurt. We all wanted relief. We all wanted to be alone. We all wanted him. We all wanted to wake up.

Michelle and Kate arrived. Tears and emotion ruled everyone.

"Okay, guys. Let's do this," Kate said.

We walked to the doors to the church. We were greeted by a foyer that was already set up. A table sat by the chapel door, adorned with flower arrangements, a guest book, and of course, a photo of Dad.

The immediate family—his parents, sisters, and I—stood in a line. We received condolences as people came into the church. One by one, friends and extended family passed us, hugged us, cried with us, acknowledged us, and shared memories of Dad. It helped, maybe. But I looked forward to the last person in line. My mother even came through the line.

The last person walked into the chapel. It was time for us to follow. We said a prayer and looked through the chapel doors. Music started playing. The procession started.

We had a front-row seat. When I saw what was beyond the doors, I went numb. A framed photo of my father stood on a table next to half of his ashes. We walked a mile down to our bench.

Alan, my father's brother, for all intents and purposes, conducted the memorial. The first to speak would be my father's mother. Kate and Michelle would follow with a musical number, then I would speak. The program also included words from Mike Burton and Mrs. Burton.

I looked around the congregation. Where were the Burtons? I wasn't particularly enthused about the idea of them being invited to soil the event, but where the hell were they? It was just as well if they didn't show up. They had no business being there.

Grandma and Grandpa sat beside me on the bench. Kate and Michelle were right behind us. Phyllis was to speak first. She spoke of Dad's childhood. She was followed by the sisters with a musical number.

I went up to the stand. Alan came up to me and whispered, "Where is Mike Burton?"

I don't know I haven't seen him."

In the middle of talking, I looked to the back of the chapel and saw Mr. and Mrs. Burton struggling to get their disheveled drunk son into his seat. I was perhaps the only person in the room that was able to determine at a distance what phase drunkenness Mike was in. I saw from his mannerisms and his facial expressions that he was long passed Happy Drunk Mike. He had skipped Calm Drunk Mike and was just exiting Numb Drunk Mike. I knew the congregation was unfortunately awaiting a potentially disastrous display from Depressed Drunk Mike, Manic Drunk Mike, Paranoid Drunk Mike, or a combination of the three. I tried not to pay attention to him sitting in the corner with his parents keeping him out of fetal position as I finished my eulogy. I made my peace with my father's death and started back toward my seat in the congregation. Before I got to the bench, I looked over at my father's inebriated widower to see what he was doing. His parents coaxed him out of his seat, and he started down the aisle. He made eye contact with me and stumbled toward me. As he tried to hug me, he tripped and nearly fell to the ground before I caught him. He brushed himself off and went up to the pulpit. I sat next to my family and braced for impact.

I thought the worst of it was over. I was wrong. As Mike sat down, after his drunken tribute, his mother stood up and started for the stand. A ten-minute soapbox for human rights and LGBTQ equality commenced. I remembered that all three of the Burtons had somehow been let into the program. Hopefully my words wouldn't be forgotten, despite being followed by the Burton signature aura of obnoxious narcissism.

Luckily the memorial didn't have to end with Mrs. Burton. Alan stood up and gave his closing remarks.

After the memorial service, it was time for everyone to eat their feelings. Dozens of homemade dishes adorned the gathering hall in the church. They were prepared by church members and loved ones of my grandparents. I knew that a lot of people in some way or another were connected to my dad, but I had no idea that the church would be packed. It was overwhelming to see everybody. Hearing countless stories of my father, I knew I was living a blur. I would only remember a fraction of what happened that day. Soon enough, it was time to leave. I found close family and said goodbye. We would see each other in a couple days to lay my father's remains to rest. Kimmy, Lizzie, and I went out to our car and made our way to Carla's house.

Chapter 24

Reconnect

2015

My roommate made a rare appearance in our apartment. I'd gotten used to being alone. When he showed up, I was in heavy thought. I decided to take a walk through the apartment complex. I walked out the door and found myself in the breezeway. Once I let Kimmy into my life, everything would get hit by the ripple effect. Kimmy represented a milestone I never thought I would reach. I couldn't help but think about my father. Our relationship used to be simple. We had made the mutual decision to drift away from each other. We hadn't talked in nearly three years. It wouldn't matter in the long term, because I knew I would die, and everything would be final. Now everything was different.

The loss of my death sentence was somewhat problematic. As excuses go, "I'm going to be dead in six months." was a magic bullet to get out of pretty much anything, including but not limited to my dysfunctional relationship with my father. I knew at some point in time, I'd have to deal with Dad. Kimmy wouldn't understand the emotions that had become the foundation of my relationship with my father.

I picked up my phone and scrolled to the bottom of my contact list. "Z Michael Parkin."

The phone started ringing. I had a different number that he didn't recognize.

The voice mail message played.

"You have reached the voice mailbox of Michael Parkin. I'm sorry I missed you. Leave a message, and I will get back to you as soon as I can."

I figured he was screening for bill collectors.

"Hello. It's your son. I have some news. If you want to call me back, this number is a good one to reach me on. Bye."

I looked at my watch and sat on a bench, setting my phone down beside me. One minute passed. Two minutes. Five minutes. Eight minutes. We were done. There was no coming back from where we'd gone. Whatever.

I stood up and headed for my apartment. My pocket was a bit light. My phone sat abandoned on the bench. The phone lit up on its way to my jeans. Pulsing and ringing, I looked at the screen. "Z Michael Parkin."

I took in a breath. "Hello?"

"Kameron?"

"Yep. It's me. You feel like talking?"

"Uh, Sure… What's up?"

"I have some news."

"Yeah? What's going on?"

"I'm getting married, Dad."

"Wow."

"Yeah. She is amazing."

"You want to tell me about her?"

"She is unlike anyone I've met. I can't explain it, but there's just some weird effect she has on me. She makes me better. I need to be better. She has a smile that lights up the room. There's this odd innocence about her. Like she doesn't understand the bad parts of me. And when I try to explain things to her, I end up having to explain them to myself. And it frustrates me because it usually doesn't make sense. This doesn't make sense. You and I. She doesn't understand the cold war. You and I have a lot of baggage to sort—that's not going to magically disappear. But I am getting married. I guess what I need to ask is, should I send an invitation to you?"

"Absolutely."

2018
July 31, Tuesday, 5:00 p.m.

Mom pulled into the driveway of Grandma Carla's house. I was dead tired, lying on the couch. I watched her park her car. I couldn't quite get a fix on Mom's emotions by her facial expressions. Mom was a master—when she wanted to be, of her emotions. That night, she seemed stoic.

I saw her walk up the sidewalk. I wondered what exactly was going on in her mind. I knew she loved my father at one point. I knew they both played a part in the demise of the marriage.

Kimmy sat on the couch next to me. Lizzie was playing on the brown carpet floor.

I was completely in love with them. I knew that at one point, I belonged to a family filled with the same love which I possessed for the family I created. My parents didn't get married to get divorced. Only Mom knew how the death of Dad was affecting her. I didn't ever expect the world would get a glimpse into that truth. As Mom came through the front door, I couldn't help but speculate what that truth might be. Whatever reality may have been, the emotion that my mother's face wore that night was a garment fashioned of mourning.

Though it was only a supposition on my part, she looked as if they hadn't divorced. My mom did not appear to be mourning for a man that she once loved but grieving the man that once loved her—a man trapped within a cage of tragic missteps. I knew that man, the father, the husband that Dad used to be. He was held captive by his own doing. At least there was a hope that he would find himself on the other side. Dad dying only reminded us of how much we missed him. I looked around the room and respected Carla's living room for what it had come to be, an altar of change. I recalled the first time I acquainted Kimmy with Grandma and Mom.

Chapter 25

A Maternal Introduction

2015

The next day I introduced Kimmy to my mother. I didn't quite know how to do it. As far as my mother knew, I was single; I didn't even have a girlfriend. A girlfriend was a fairly minor thorn in a mother's side. Girlfriends were companions that could come and go—no permanence, no commitment. But fiancées, well, fiancées almost always turn into wives. Wives commandeer sons from their mothers. I didn't know how that prospect would sit with my mother, but I assumed it likely wouldn't go over well. Kimmy and I did move fast. We knew it was right. But explaining that to my mother was going to be very tedious operation, one I wasn't looking forward to. I wouldn't ever have described my relationship with my mother as healthy, however, it was among the most important in my life. I'd experienced a life where I had exiled my mother before, and it wasn't pretty. I didn't ever want to do that again. We had our issues, but I didn't want to hurt her any further and I certainly was wary of doing anything that might cause undue stress on the relationship. Springing a 'Hey mom, this is my new girlfriend, and oh, by the way, she is my fiancé and we are getting married in 6 months' didn't seem all that fair. I hoped that she would take it well. She had to. Kimmy was perfect for me. There wasn't anything serious that was unlikeable about Kimmy.

Mom was at Carla's house. I picked Kimmy up from her apartment to take her back to Carla's place. As we approached the house, I couldn't help but feeling like I was leading my future wife to her appointment with the gallows. I saw mom's red Ford Escape in the driveway and my heart sunk. The car meant that indeed the executioner was on duty. I took a deep breath and looked over at Kimmy. "I'm 98 percent sure she's not armed. If you see any sudden movements, just get on the ground and I'll cover you."

"I'm sure she is not going to really react like that, Kam."

"Well, she does know how to use a gun, but she also likes to be theatrical. We might have to deal with a knife. If she offers you food or a glass of water, politely decline. If she insists, take it but don't eat or drink it."

"Come on, baby, I'm sure she's going to be fine. It's all in your head."

"Kimberly, no. You don't get it. You represent the thing that my mother has dreaded for the last twenty years—the prospect of losing me. She ain't gonna like you. You're lovable. Don't take it personally, you two may really click. But after all is said and done, at the end of the night if a ring is on your finger, she is going to want your head on her wall."

"Whatever, let's just go inside and meet her." Kimmy rolled her eyes further back than I had ever seen.

"Okay," I replied nervously.

Kimmy had already started toward the front door of Carla's house. I rushed to get in front of her. I needed something between her and my mother until I could gauge how homicidal Mom was. When we walked through the front door, Mom was sitting in the living room.

"Hey, Mom! How are you doing today?"

"Just fine, how are you, son? I see you have someone with you."

"Yeah! I do! This is Kimmy…my fiancée."

"Oh, wow! You didn't mention over the phone that she was your fiancée."

"Well, I did say that I was introducing you to someone special…who's more special than a fiancée?"

Mom looked at me for a minute and then said, "I suppose you're right!" Mom worked furiously to stifle her shock. Her gaze shifted from me to Kimmy. After a moment, my poor mother shook it off and smiled. "Hi, Kimmy, it is an honor to meet you."

Like a tiger shot with a tranquilizer dart, my mother fought for lucidity as she gestured toward the living room chairs." Come in, come in. I want to hear all about how this happened—about how you two met. How long have you been dating? Where did you meet?"

Mom looked back at me. I couldn't gauge her emotions. I pictured cartoonlike stars spinning around her head while her mind grappled with what I threw at her. I felt bad for not telling her I was going to propose. Somehow it just didn't come up beforehand.

"We actually met on a blind date," I said.

Mom cut me off. "Kameron, I asked the lady." I caught Mom's first facial expression. She shot a dagger at me. Yep, I knew I would have to pay for this later. Mom shifted her glance back over to Kimmy, studying her, examining her. It was as if my mother were trying to dissect all the qualities she could see in Kimmy—to determine why or how Kimmy had captured me.

"Yeah, we did meet on a blind date," Kimmy replied.

"Oh, a blind date? Kameron, you've been going on blind dates?"

"It was actually just a fluke thing. Kimmy's roommate was dating my roommate. She set me up with Kimmy. Her roommate, believe it or not, set us up because of our cerebral palsy. I guess she saw us and thought that we were the last two of the species and that we should be together because we were both disabled."

"Yeah, my roommate was pretty crazy, but we went out one time, and it went surprisingly well."

"Oh well, that's nice!" Mom was using her Mrs. Whitney voice. Her phone voice. The voice that she used when she was pissed off into oblivion but had to keep a positive façade. I knew I was in deep shit. I just hoped my mother wouldn't hurt Kimmy.

"I don't know what it was, but the universe brought us together. She's literally my better half." I gestured toward her left hand—the one unscathed by cerebral palsy.

"Well, it looks like you two were just made for each other! Forgive me, it's a lot to digest, but I'm so happy for you, Kam. Happy for the both of you! Come here."

Mom got up from the couch and came toward me. I instinctively got up, and she hugged me very tightly. Now the cartoon stars were spinning around my head. Was Mom actually happy for me? This had to be a fake reaction, right? "I look forward to hearing the rest of your story. Kam said that you've got a party to get to tonight?"

"Yeah, one of my roommates is moving out were having a going-away party for her," Kimmy said.

"Oh well, darn. Kimmy, I am so glad to meet you, and I am excited to get to know you. We'll see each other soon! Okay?" Mom took Kimmy into a hug. It was the first time they had physical contact and also the first-time mom was within choking distance. I held my breath.

"Yeah, so nice to meet you, too."

"Stacey, call me Stacey. Or whatever you're comfortable with."

"Okay, Stacey."

Mom released Kimmy. Kimmy did not appear injured. I was grateful and stupefied at the same time. I saw mom fidgeting with her hands. She was wearing the ring, her emerald ring. The piece of jewelry that was probably among her most treasured possessions. It was a ring that had my birth stone in it. My father gave it to her years ago and, yet somehow, the piece had survived the negative emotions of divorce. I didn't know the whole story behind it, But I did know it was something that my father gave to her which represented the family—the family that she started 20 years ago. She spoke.

"Hey Kimmy, one thing before you go." She took off her emerald. "Kameron's dad gave this ring to me years ago. It has an emerald in it, which happens to be Kam's birthstone. I've worn it since I got it. Today, I think It should go to you. Maybe someday, you can pass it down. But I'd like to start the tradition today. I am truly excited to meet you. Welcome to the family."

I struggled to keep my jaw from hitting the ground. Wow. Mom gave Kimmy her Emerald? I hadn't considered the prospect of having a family that was actually functional again. I wasn't prepared for order. We left and caught the bus to back to Kimmy's apartment, Kimmy said, "See, Kam, there was nothing to worry about."

2018
July 31, Tuesday, 9:00 p.m.

The week was taxing to my mind. My soul. My body. I was at a tipping point. I thought my health was in a pretty good place. I'd been feeling fine the whole time. I just couldn't believe it was over. My dad was gone. Ashes to ashes—whatever that meant.

I got up from the couch. Carla's couch meant a lot to her. It was the first piece of furniture she purchased in quite a while. Of high quality, the couch was extremely comfortable.

The piece was elegant—unlike its very identifiable predecessor with a print on it that may as well have "1991" in block lettering sewn into the back cushions. I remembered when Grandma replaced the old couch. The old one was known in the family as "Joe's couch"; he practically lived on it. The couch was worn and tattered. The black oversized monster dominated the room—until it didn't. When Grandpa died, Grandma Carla, while not filling her vow to bury him in it, soon parted ways with the sofa.

When she bought the new couch that was now in the living room, Carla used her own money and her sole input. The last couch was him. This one was her. Whenever I looked at the couch, I saw Grandma Carla. It suited her. I left the living room for the guest room. I was well overdue for bed. My pills were awaiting me on the nightstand.

It had been exactly twelve hours since my last dose. As I went into the guest room, I knew. I felt it. What was left of the two white pills and one blue pill I took at 9:00 a.m. were doing their best to keep me up.

The chemicals released. Fighting the electrical storm in my head. Dampening the lightning strikes and protecting my brain from electrocution, the medication fought it off. Though I wasn't electrocuted, I sat on the floor, shocked. The pills were working. I had been cured. I was living with the storm in check. No more wells. No more falls. No more harm. I had a life, a future, an expiration date yet to be determined.

Just when I'd let my guard down, the storm made itself known. It flashed to remind me I was not Zeus. Though I could control the lightning to a point. I was not its god. As I scrambled for my pills, I knew that I hadn't been pushed over the edge. But I saw it—the flash. The feeling of falling. The neuro-stutter, whose absence I'd grown to take for granted. I sat on my bed in fear. I backed away from the edge.

I prayed that the lightning was not the start of a storm.

I waited in silence for the thunderclap.

Chapter 26

From Four Wheels to Two

2009

Driving was amazing. I felt freedom. I felt invincible. Unfortunately, I couldn't feel quite legal at fourteen. If I wanted to go anywhere on my own, it had to be on foot or by bicycle. Dad's old ten-speed was in one of Grandma and Grandpa's outbuildings. I wanted to go on a little adventure by myself, but gauging from the seat position on the bike, my dad was significantly taller than I was the last time he rode it.

After exhuming the bicycle from the metal cemetery, I brought it to the garage where Grandpa was working. After hosing down the vintage ten-speed, I discovered Dad's bicycle was not an off shade of orange. In fact, the bike was ruby red. Though it needed a bit of TLC, it had a lot of potential.

After getting rid of the twenty-two years of dust and grime, the next order of business was to adjust the seat, air up the tires, and take a ride and see what needed fixing. Grandpa was tinkering on something else when I started looking for a wrench.

"Hey, Grandpa, I need to move this seat down. Do you have a wrench I can use?"

Grandpa walked over to his toolbox. "Yeah, sure, what are you looking to do? Are you really gonna bring that old thing back to life?"

"I'm going to try." Something wasn't right. Grandpa's toolbox started to get really far away. The lights started flashing. Everything started swirling. I smelled chlorine. Grandpa's hot tub was in the backyard. Hundreds of feet away. Why was I smelling the hot tub?

"Grandpa."

"Yeah?"

"Grandp—I feel, I'm…I'm going to. I'm going t—"

"*Kameron!*"

I heard the wrench drop on the concrete. I wondered if it was the right size. I didn't want to lose it.

I didn't know where I was going. The garage turned dark green. The lights went on. I fell, but I didn't stop falling. I knew I had to stop and hit the ground sometime, but it wasn't coming. The floor wasn't getting closer. I just kept falling, down a bottomless flashing well. Lights everywhere. Sounds everywhere. The well was chlorinated. That was odd. Who would swim in a well?

Beeping. I woke up. Hospital room. Everyone appeared worried. I figured I'd gotten out of the well. Someone pulled me out. Did Grandpa? Wait, there wasn't a well at Grandma and Grandpa Parkin's house. Definitely not in their garage. That was where I fell down, right?

After I saw Mom, Dad, Grandma, and Grandpa in the room looking at me intently. The doctor spoke, "How are you feeling? Can you tell me your name?"

"Kameron."

"I'm Dr. Sorenson"

"I have kind of a headache." As I responded, my body coughed at me in protest. The pain hit me. Every single joint and muscle in my body was sore. What happened to me? I felt like I was hit by a truck.

Dr. Sorenson continued, "A headache? Okay. How about pain elsewhere?"

I let out a grumble in response.

"Okay. Kameron, do you remember anything about what happened?"

I wanted to say something about the well. But I didn't want to look stupid. I shook my head.

"Kameron, you had a seizure. A very long seizure. We're happy to see you waking up in here. Do you know what a seizure is?"

"Like shaking and stuff. Right?"

"Yeah, you are just coming out of the sedative we gave you, the important thing to know is you are safe. We're monitoring you. And we'll figure this out. I'll be back in a while to check up on you, okay?"

"Okay."

"Just get some rest for now."

"Thanks."

They all left the room as I was closing my eyes.

Dr. Sorenson's voice could be overheard coming from the hallway. "A forty-five-minute seizure is nothing to be taken lightly. He is lucky to be here. But there is still hope. We'll figure this out. The most important thing is that he is watched closely."

I saw my parents and grandparents in the hallway. They shared the same facial expression. Grandpa may have kept me safe, but I saw in his eyes he was shaken.

I had a field of open wells in front of me. This was just the beginning. The color draining from everybody's face told me they were just as scared as I was. I knew my parents were trying to figure out whether to fold or double down on their marriage.

I also knew that they didn't need to have this hand dealt to them. I hated being the bad hand. This only complicated things for them. If nothing else, the series of events to follow would be captivating to watch. In the back of my mind, the inevitable moment vexed me. The moment would come—when the chips would fall.

That moment would be painful and life-altering.

2018
August 1, Wednesday, 9:00 a.m.

The freeway carried my past on its shoulders. With each mile marker going by, a faint shadow of a memory entered my mind. A time that was pure and unadulterated by fear and stress—I could almost remember.

I exited the freeway and started down Main Street. The grocery store where we used to shop, the Chevron where we fueled all our cars, the 7-Eleven where I bought Slurpees without my parents knowing. I passed a furniture store in what the town knew as the old Parkin Motor building. I saw the church where my father had just been memorialized. With a few turns down the side streets I saw even more. I saw my old high school. I drove by the hospital that I was born in. I drove past the house that sheltered the first five years of my childhood. I drove past the house that became the minefield where my childhood came to an early demise. I also saw the road that led to my grandparents' house. Everything in that town was the same. But it was also different.

Everything around me used to symbolize home. Now those symbols were reminders, reminders that that place was no longer my home. The Chevron was just a gas station. The 7-Eleven was just one of many convenience stores. The old Parkin motor building was just a building that used to hold a family business. The building where I attended high school was just a school—it wasn't *my* old high school. That town no longer owned me. I no longer owned it. We weren't together anymore. Nephi wasn't my hometown anymore. It was only a vague origin, all but forgotten.

I parked on the side of the road that led to my grandparents' place. I sat in the car and paused. As I stared at the brown brick house, I made a conscious shift in my mind. Last time I was there, I'd removed everything I cared about. I made a physical break from their house during the last visit. This time, I needed to make an emotional breakaway.

For the sake of my sanity, I had to remove any sentimental ties. I wasn't going to Grandma and Grandpa's house. I was going to visit my grandparents. In *their* home. Before I started toward the house, I prepared. "Nothing here is connected to you. You are just here for the family."

I exhaled and shifted back into drive. I parked in the driveway. When I approached the front door, the dog didn't bark. When I rang the doorbell, I didn't hear Grandpa get up to hush the dog. They weren't home. It made sense.

When Grandma and Grandpa sought solace, they never looked to their home.

I called their phone. "Hey, Grandma, we're here. You don't appear to be home."

"Oh, we just headed out. We're on our way to the cemetery. We decided to just meet there instead of the house. Just meet us there. Kate and Michelle are on their way."

"Okay, I'll be right over."

"See you in a few minutes."

"Yeah. Bye, Grandma."

They knew I was coming. Why didn't they update me? Kimmy and I made our way to the cemetery. The area felt vacant. All souls had departed their bodies long before we arrived. Kate and Michelle were supposedly on their way.

I figured Grandma and Grandpa were taking one last ride with their son before they had to bring him to his final resting place.

We parked our car on the side of the road and walked toward the family plots. One had been opened for dad. A plywood board rested on top of the opening. Some artificial grass was lying on top—awaiting Dad's urn. I visited other family members who had gone before dad. My grandmother's parents. My grandfather's parents. When Great-Grandma Parkin died, that was the first funeral I'd gone to. I was eight years old. It was the first time I saw my dad crying painful tears. I couldn't recall whether I saw my grandfather cry or not, but I had a feeling that I would see that today.

I remember bagpipes playing at Great Grandma's funeral. Dad said that he wanted bagpipes at his funeral. He also said that he wanted to be buried next to his grandma. I thought it was peculiar he didn't mention a desire for cremation prior to being laid to rest. At least we were able to give him part of what he wanted.

Katie and Michelle arrived. Still, no grandparents. They got out of the car, and we engaged in a group embrace. We put our game faces on. Dad had been gone for a few days now. Today was the day we would finalize things.

I didn't know where Mike Burton was, or where his share of my father's remains was, or how Mike Burton would decide to dispose of my father's remains. Suddenly it didn't matter. I was at peace with it. Mike Burton had gotten his piece of my father, but we got the good part of Dad back. I looked at the gate of the cemetery and saw Grandma and Grandpa's truck pulling in. The man of the hour had arrived.

The vehicle stopped. Grandpa shifted into park and killed the engine. I watched my grandparents as they sat in the cab for a few moments holding their son's remains. Grandpa's hands were on the urn. Grandma's left arm was wrapped around it as it sat on the center console. As they got out of the truck, Grandpa held the urn preciously as if he were carrying priceless vase. His world was in that vase. The remains of his only son. All that was left of the child he first welcomed into the world—he would be required to submit back into the earth. Grandma was at his side. They seemed as if they were separated from the world. They made their way to dad's grave in sacred silence that seemed impenetrable. After they placed Dad's remains upon the grave, they returned and joined us. It didn't seem necessary to interact with each other. We were all experiencing the same emotion. All our hearts were quaking on the same fault lines. We were all just gathered together at Dad's graveside almost waiting for something to come, waiting for the final buzzer, some sort of signal to indicate this was indeed the end. Grandpa left the group and walked back toward his truck. The rest of us were so immersed in the moment that I was the only one to notice he left.

He started the truck and then walked back toward us. I was puzzled and continued to watch as he pulled out his phone. After a series of scrolls and tabs, I realized what he was doing. From behind the group, bagpipes began to sound. "Amazing Grace" filled the air as tears filled the family's eyes. We all looked at the urn as the bagpipes continued. I don't know why, but the image of a family gathered around a radio came to mind.

I wondered why in all the old photographs; most people looked at the radio during a nightly broadcast. What were they watching? What were they hoping for? It was an inanimate object sitting a few feet away from them. It made sound, sure, but the radio never stimulated the other senses. Why choose to occupy the sense of vision with a stationary radio? At that moment, staring at my father's urn placed beside his grave, I understood the photographs. We were watching for the same reason that the people watched the radio. We all watched, to let our sixth sense take over.

Sight was pacified by the urn.

Hearing was captivated by the bagpipes.

Smell had been overtaken by flowers and freshly cut lawn.

The taste of saltwater arrived with migrating tears.

The touch of a familiar hand offered comfort.

The only sense left unchecked was imagination. As I watched my father's grave, my mind drifted. His life flashed before my eyes. I saw my memories of him in my early childhood, our darker days. I saw the bad parts of our relationship. I saw him see his granddaughter for the first time. I saw him react to the news of gaining a second grandchild. I saw the culmination of my father as a man. Who he was as my father, as a son, as a brother, as a husband, as a grandfather.

I made a decision to lay to rest the good parts of him. To memorialize the parts of my father that really mattered to me. I would let Mike Burton bury the other half that he corrupted. The remains of the person we were laying to rest at that moment belonged to my father. The man that I would tell my children about. The man that he deserved to be remembered as.

I watched as my father's broadcast concluded. The bagpipes stopped. We signed off.

Chapter 27

A Lasting First Impression

2015

She said yes. I was told the parents did too. But I hadn't met the parents. I wasn't sure how violent her father was—if he would go to prison for her. I should have asked for her hand, but I thought that it wasn't something that really should be done over the phone. Jane and Chris were in California. I couldn't meet them in person. What was the point in asking them over the phone? They couldn't gather much about me over the phone. So I'd forgone asking permission.

That night we met at a restaurant. I was poised to plead for forgiveness. At least meeting in a public place had a positive upshot for me—I likely wouldn't be beaten up or murdered...there.

We arrived at the restaurant just as Kimmy's parents pulled into the parking lot. Kimmy's father was searching from behind the wheel for his daughter (and what she insisted on bringing home from college). I couldn't see his eyes very well from behind the glass of his car. I wasn't exactly straining for eye contact. I'd been preoccupied with this moment since before I proposed. Chris pulled into a parking place and turned off the car. As we drew closer to them, the Shermans became clearer.

Kimmy's mom jumped out of the car and hugged Kimmy. Then Jane approached me—with unexpected enthusiasm. "Oh, it's so nice to meet you!"

"Thank you. It's nice to meet you too. Kimmy has told me a lot about both of you."

I was still trying to figure out whether or not they were angry that I hadn't introduced myself to them over the phone.

"Welcome to the family!" Jane said.

Chris had gotten out of the car and given Kimmy a hug while Jane was introducing herself.

My father-in-law-to-be walked up to me. Body language communicated Chris's emotion very well. He seemed approachable, but he had a look in his eyes that told me "If you are playing a game, I will knock your pieces over faster than you can say 'checkmate.'"

When we shook hands, he once again spoke to me without using his mouth. The grip he took on my hand said much more than "Hello. Nice to meet you." Chris used the grip to convey a concealed warning. "If you hurt my daughter, I will end you. If you treat her like she is meant to be treated, you will be accepted into this family. Understand this right now, boy—or walk."

"Welcome to the family!" Chris uttered with a smile.

Jane jumped right into conversation before we even got through the door of the restaurant. "Kimmy has been secretive about you, but from what I hear you're quite a guy."

"Oh, really?" I looked over at Kimmy.

"Okay, Mom, let's go order," Kimmy said, blushing.

"What else did Kimmy say about me?" I asked. Kimmy glared at me. I loved that glare. Something told me that it would stop being cute after the honeymoon.

"Oh, don't worry. All good things," Jane assured.

"Let's go order, guys." Chris sounded like he wanted to get on with the evening. I identified with him.

Jane took charge of the conversation.

"So do you prefer Kameron or Kam?"

"Eh, it doesn't matter to me."

"Okay, Kam, Welcome to the family."

"And what do you prefer to be called? Jane? Chris? Mama Jane? Pa? Sir? Ha ha."

Chris cut in. "Sir. You can call me sir."

Either I irrevocably blew my shot at being on Chris's good graces. Or my future father-in-law was a force of deadpan humor to be reckoned with.

"Yes, sir."

Kimmy rolled her eyes. "You can call him whatever you want."

"I think I'll stick with sir."

Chris looked like he was evaluating me. I couldn't help but think that his assessment had to be poor. There I was, having proposed to his daughter without his permission. His experience with me, up to that point, consisted of four—maybe seven cumulative minutes of in-passing contact between various Facetime calls between Kimmy and her parents. I was the man in the background. Or rather, the "boy."

I was definitely of a different background than my bride-to-be. That background brought me to my knees. How was I supposed to explain the dysfunctional family I came from to the Shermans? Kimmy knew that my dad was gay. She knew that my dad's husband was gay too. But had she told her parents? That would have been a worthwhile question to ask my fiancée on the ride over. I prayed that if the Shermans had indigestion that night, it would come from a rancid hamburger patty and not the goober son-in-law their daughter had found in college.

2018
August 2, Thursday, 9:00 a.m.

My phone rang; it was my mother. "Hi, son, how are you doing?"

"As well as I can be, I guess."

"You mentioned earlier, that you wanted to get Dad's things from Mike Burton. Have you gotten them yet?"

"No, not yet. I'm still working on it."

"Would you like some help?"

"Help? What do you mean?"

"You at Granny's?"

"Yeah."

"I'll come by later today, and we'll come up with a plan."

"Okay."

"I'll see you in a little while. Bye."

"All-righty. Bye."

An hour later, Mom pulled into the driveway. She walked through the front door.

She sat down on her favorite chair across from me. "I may be able to get Mike Burton. After all, I was also a spouse to your father. I think that's enough common ground to build a relationship with Mike Burton. Plus, Mike Burton is, as you already know, extremely stupid and very arrogant. When you put both of those personality traits together, you get someone who is very easily manipulated. I'm sure if we work on him a little bit, we can get anything we want out of Mike Burton."

"Interesting, I'm on board."

"What, Kameron? You didn't really think your father was the only manipulator in the family, did you?"

"No, I guess I just didn't fully appreciate your skill set."

"I'm capable of a lot more than you think I am, kid."

"So it would seem." I looked at my mother in a slightly different light after she said that.

I saw her dark side. For years, I knew my mother as a broken person—the damage of whom I'd inflicted a significant portion. I always felt ashamed of what I had done to my mother.

A new emotion replaced my remorse. My habitual shame faded. Intrigue. I looked into my mother's eyes. I saw it. A partition. One like mine. She had it too. She could play people. Maybe I wasn't the most cunning person in the room. Maybe I never was. We remained locked in eye contact.

A wordless conversation took place. Had the exchange taken place verbally, we would have sat for hours. Mom told me everything I needed to know, using just her eyes. Her words replayed in my head.

"I'm capable of a lot more than you think I am, kid."

I broke. Twelve words. I hadn't given credit to the right person. Until then, Mike Burton was the king of psychological manipulation. And I was the prince.

Maybe I wasn't a psychological prince by marriage. Maybe my mental edge came through blood, royal blood—from my mother. My mother cut through my astonishment. I knew Mom had her demons. I had seen her at her low and caused her to hit rock bottom.

The woman I saw that day was different. She had been quenched into hardened steel. Everything made sense. I was too close to her in my childhood to realize, I was watching a process during those years. Her demons that I chastised her for, punished her, blamed her for. Mom was being forged. Mom had been the sharpest sword in the armory all along. Everything fell into perspective.

Mike Burton had no idea he was condemned.

Chapter 28

Union

July 11, 2015

I saw her. We'd just been bound in holy matrimony for time and all eternity. We drove off from our wedding reception to begin our honeymoon. The rear windshield was obstructed by painted silver hearts. "Just Married" I only needed to see in front of us, down the road ahead. I'd gazed into many roads that disappeared into a horizon. This road felt different.

I held her hand and saw her beautiful smile beam into me. My heart began firing on all cylinders for the first time. My soul got its first taste of premium fuel. Kimmy provided me with an octane higher than anything I'd ever run on. It was exhilarating. We sped down the freeway. Limitless, I looked back through the windshield at the road ahead. It wasn't straight. I knew it wouldn't always be smooth. But I knew that I had her. We could go anywhere, see anything.

For the first time, I gripped the wheel not out of fear but out of excitement. Our honeymoon marked the practice lap. The next week, we would familiarize ourselves with each other, truly see what it was like to drive together. I knew that the starting flag was going to wave soon, but when I looked into her eyes, I looked back at the course with excitement.

What we had ahead of us was a race that we would win. My hold on the wheel adjusted as I felt for the signal stalk. A pass left to the fast lane. I felt the four-cylinder Hyundai's rhythm. That day, a six-speed V8 was mounted in the engine bay.

We sped to our future in ecstasy.

2018
August 3, Friday, 9:00 a.m.

I hadn't spent enough time in Utah for my physical clock to adjust to waking up an hour later. I woke myself up before my phone did it for me. Carla's house was quiet. Kimmy was still asleep. Lizzie was asleep. And my father was dead. He was gone, laid to rest. It was time to leave. There was nothing left to do.

I attempted to connect with the Parkins one last time before leaving. In a post-Michael Parkin world, we had to learn how to bridge the gap, to communicate with each other again. We would need to figure out how or even *if* we could all coexist in a room, which was cramped—due to the humongous elephant sitting in the corner. It wasn't like nobody wanted to talk about him. No one knew how to talk about him.

My experience with the Parkins told me it could quite possibly be a long while before the family knew how to acknowledge Dad without letting the subject consume all the available oxygen, like a fire burning through a circus tent—probably the most appropriate venue for our minds. Everything was turning into a circus.

The endless display of family and doctors dancing around us. Mike Burton, a magician pulling off impossible illusions, bending reality, making it his own. And me, a stagehand, negotiating all the behind-the-scenes pieces.

I picked my phone up off the nightstand. I didn't expect them to respond. But they did. Maybe they would see value in a relationship with me, after all.

"Hey, Grandma. U want to meet up 4 lunch today b4 we head out?"

"Sure thing! I'll C if Kate and Michelle can go 2."

"Gr8."

I was gobsmacked. They actually wanted to meet. Most of the time I was there, they avoided me. But today was different. Maybe it would stay that way. Maybe it was a fluke. I still couldn't trust it.

I looked over at my wife. She was still asleep. So was Lizzie. I sneaked out of bed.

I walked through the kitchen and reached the stairs. I grabbed the railing and tiptoed down the steps—on the left side. I knew exactly where each stair creaked. I was in the basement once again. It was still empty. I walked to my room and went in. The bed was more inviting when I lived there. The mouse tracks were a recent addition.

I walked to the center of the room and sat down. I knew comfort was a relative thing. People could be comfortable anywhere. I used to feel safer in that makeshift bedroom than anywhere else in the world.

In a few hours, I would drive toward California to a place that I didn't deserve to call home. I was raised to believe that in order to accept charity, one had to sacrifice dignity. I still couldn't communicate well with the Shermans. We came from different worlds.

In my world, "thank you" was a dirty word. When one was given something, they were to take it with their head hung in shame—a Sherman, on the other hand, would just give freely from kindness of heart. No strings attached. It was uncanny. Chris and Jane had opened their home to us.

They'd renovated their garage to make more living space. I couldn't figure them out. I needed a way to get out on our own. I prayed for something to give me enough traction to get my family under a roof I provided.

Chapter 29

Relocate

2016

October. I liked being married. I liked having a child. I liked my life. However, similar to the pair of chinos in my closet, which I also liked—I had no clue how to provide enough steam to keep them wrinkle-free. I was headed toward a brick wall in school. It seemed like everything was going downhill, and I didn't know where to go. If I wanted to make decent money with my declared major in history education, I would have to get a doctorate to be eligible for a decent job as a professor at a university. I had switched my major too many times, and I wasn't going anywhere. When I learned that Kimmy had talked about it with her mother, I found that a change of scenery might be the best option. Little did I know, in a month's time, we'd move to California.

I wasn't the first motivated to relocate to California by the prospect of finding gold. Many others had gone before me. Maybe, just maybe there was still enough left that I could claim. Whether it was a nugget or just a little bit of gold dust, I had to figure out how to support the new family I'd just built. I had no plan. I wasn't even sure if I had a goal.

At the time most people were thinking about their career path, I was told my life path was closed. I found an inn and waited for death.

Maybe I should have prayed for a life coach before I pra,
companion.

I didn't know what I could or wanted to do for a living. I spent my entire life being told by people who either didn't go to college or dropped out of college that "your life will be terrible if you don't get a degree." For the most part, all of them were dissatisfied with their lives. But Kimmy's family was different.

The Sherman mind-set allowed room for a bit more imagination. Maybe if I were around the Shermans I could figure out a path to a career and a life—one that wouldn't make me want to take a nice soothing bubble bath with my toaster.

Jane was a master real estate and business guru. Her mind was the backbone of entrepreneurship. Mortgage and loan businesses, real estate businesses, startup ventures. It appeared as though my mother-in-law could fashion a profitable business out of anything, anywhere.

2018
August 3, Friday, 2:00 p.m.

We met at their favorite restaurant, Chick-fil-A. It was the last time them before I left for California. As a precaution before ordering, I patted my front pocket to make sure I had my wallet. I never knew who was to pick up the check when I dined with the Parkins. Better safe than sorry. Grandma and Grandpa ordered first, then Grandpa motioned for me and Kimmy to come place our orders. I guessed grandpa was picking up the tab. Michelle and her family ordered and then Kate and her family. We sat down awaiting our meals. Everyone couldn't help but notice that one family member was noticeably absent. We sat in silence mostly. Some small talk here and there. Sandwiches filled our mouths, so words didn't have to. After about ten minutes we began to get a rhythm. When we finished our meals, I began exit proceedings.

Kimmy and I reserved a hotel room in Winnemucca. It was time for Kimmy and me to leave. After bidding everyone goodbye and getting on our way, I couldn't help but wonder if the lines of communication would stay open.

I hoped for the best. We pulled out of the parking lot and headed back home. As we got further away from my childhood home, I was able to breathe a little deeper. I had done what I had gone there to do. Now it was time to go forward. My life in California was far from established.

The entirety of my marriage was a series of failure after failure. The cycle needed to cease. I knew I was running out of time to figure something out. The Shermans were likely growing impatient with me. Everything I'd done since I married their daughter had only yielded loss.

When I looked at my father's life with the naked eye after removing my rose-colored glasses, I could see that his life was a series of disappointments. If there was one thing that I could do to honor him, to make his life mean something, it was to learn from his life. I had to break the cycle. But I needed help.

I looked over at Kimmy. She loved road trips. They were exciting to her. She got to see new things, travel at high speed, and listen to her favorite music—all while not being at the wheel. I coveted that. I longed for the days before I was at the wheel—when I was only a passenger in someone else's life.

Chapter 30

The Last Supper

June 2018

Seeing Victor always reminded me of how bad a person I was. Then I would see the person that I wanted to be. Victor was my first real friend that I had in my adult life. He was the type of guy who, as they say, had his head on straight. Being around people like Victor made me acutely aware of how cross-threaded my head was.

I was a bad friend to Victor. I knew I got more out of the friendship than I contributed to it. He knew it too. But for some reason, Victor kept up contact. I wasn't sure why I gravitated toward people who were better than me. Maybe some level of my subconscious wanted to remind me of the ample room for improvement I possessed. I knew Victor was a blessing.

Though I rarely called him, I always answered his calls. When he called me to let me know he was getting married, I was thrilled for him. He was my only friend. We had to go to the wedding. Once again, we were called back to Utah. Timing happened to be very good. Going to Utah would provide Kimmy and me the perfect opportunity to break the news about the baby in person.

According to my phone, we reached our destination. I looked around the neighborhood and instantly knew which house belonged to Michelle. Dad wasn't there yet. But everyone else was. I was about to crash a family party. This hadn't been my family in quite some time. When I left the family, I didn't think that there would be a time that I would come back.

I never expected the Parkins to hold my seat at the family dinner table. After I reconnected with them when I got married, I was surprised. My seat was gone. They were still a complete family without me. Birthdays, Christmases, family parties, and everything else had seamlessly gone on as normal without me. They had moved on. I'd seen bits and pieces of their lives through social media. I knew my cousins were getting older. The family had gone places together, but when I saw them in person, it really hit me. I'd fallen behind. I saw my younger cousins interact with their grandparents, the same way I used to. They had a true bond. Like we used to. I was suddenly filled with emotion, that at first glance appeared as envy of my cousins, and feelings of abandonment from my grandparents. But when I looked closer, I really felt regret. Regret and the longing to go back—to do things differently. I saw Grandpa talking to my younger cousin, with the same closeness that we once had. Instead of carrying that into adulthood, I let it fall by the wayside. I knew I'd never get that relationship back again, the same way that it was, and I hated myself for it.

I didn't know how to talk to them anymore. There wasn't much to talk about other than the weather. My wedding was painful to get through with them. I told myself that it wouldn't always be that way. But here I was with a wife, child, and another one on the way and I still couldn't connect with them. When I pictured what my life would have been if those relationships hadn't failed, I got even angrier. Somehow I had to get through two hours with them. At least I had Kimmy to keep me sane. We'd been there twenty minutes when Dad showed up. Unfortunately, he wasn't alone. Dad brought Mike Burton. Mike Burton went into the possessive overdrive mode whenever he was with the Parkins. Marking his territory, as it were, and also making a point of letting my dad's family know that he was their son's main priority now. As they walked in the door, I hugged my father. Then Mike Burton cut in and hugged me. As Dad greeted his sisters and his parents, Mike Burton quickly followed suit to leave his stain wherever Dad's embrace had been placed. When I made an effort to talk to my father, Mike Burton cut in.

"Hey, Kam, how have you been?"

"Fine, Mike. You?"

"Good, good. I've missed you. Tell me what's new."

"Nothing, really. You know, Kimmy is pregnant. Lizzie is growing like a weed."

Mike noticed that Dad had gotten involved in conversation with one of the sisters, and Mike promptly left me after, saying, "That's nice."

The entire evening, I had only two choices. Talk to the family that I left or talk to a father that left me for someone else. Communication was nearly impossible. All we had was the past. The distant past. Nobody wanted to remember the recent past—that was where the demons lived. However, the distant past was too far away to be relevant. Childhood memories could only sustain us for so long. Sooner or later we would be confronted by the present. Once everyone was synchronized, inevitably our breaking point came. The future was not a topic to be discussed. Nobody knew how to proceed. We didn't know how to move forward.

I longed for something from my past that I needed now. The ability to coexist. None of us could just be. I desperately wanted to spend time with them. Just in a state of being. The only thing I wanted to accomplish was to make a new memory. I didn't need to reflect; I didn't need to ponder possibilities. I just wanted to live, to make progress. I wanted to explore. But to the Parkins, it seemed that they viewed our relationship as an island; the cartography was complete. The only thing left was to revisit.

Mike Burton's agenda was to stay on the island only long enough to resupply his boat. He knew that if Dad stayed on land long enough, he might not want to go back out to sea.

I watched as Mike Burton blocked everyone from dad. When Mike was distracted, I made my move.

"Hey, Dad, it's been a really long time since we've just talked. I would really like to do lunch while we are here."

"Yeah, that sounds good! Let's meet up tomorrow!"

"Costa Vida?"

"Most definitely!"

"I smiled." Maybe there was a way forward with Dad.

We left Michelle's place. I felt victorious, scoring one on one time with my father.

I woke the following morning to the sound of a xylophone. I went to shower. When. I came back to Carla's guest room, I saw a notification. Dad called. A single voice mail awaited my evaluation.

"Hi, Kam, I'm not feeling that great today. Maybe we can get together later this week, or next time if you want. Call me back. Love you. Bye."

Dad didn't remember that I was leaving in two days. As usual, Mike held him in captivity. I'd been fighting for too long to win Dad back from Mike Burton. Maybe I would try again the next time I was in town. There wasn't any point in calling him back.

2018
August 3, Friday, 9:00 p.m.

When we got to the Holiday Inn, we were too tired to use the pool. After we finished our bucket of fried chicken from the KFC drive-through next door to the hotel, it didn't take long to go to sleep.

Kimmy and Lizzie were asleep on one hotel bed. I was on the other. I stared at the ceiling. I was going back to a homestead—the place where my life needed to take root. So far, all I produced was failure. I'd been given multiple chances to get my shit together; nothing had worked. Just when I was on the cusp of achieving something, an unknown compulsion inside me would press the self-destruct button. I didn't know why, but I seemed incapable of finishing anything.

My mind drifted, but I still couldn't fall asleep. The ceiling over the hotel room faded and turned into a mirror. I saw myself. I started to question why. How? What had taken me here?

I should've died. I shouldn't have ever been in a position to start the family that was sleeping in the bed next to me. Yet for some reason, at one time I thought that it would fix me to have someone. To have an attachment, something to stick around for. Here I was, staring out into a dark void, and nothing had really changed about me. The only thing that was really different was the level of depression.

Now if I had to leave, there'd be more collateral damage. More blowback. Ruin the lives of three more people. Maybe I'd have my dad on the other side. But I didn't know how to get there. I didn't want to take my life. But I wanted someone else to take it. It was a beautiful life, but I didn't know how to take ownership. Why the hell did Kimmy marry me? What business did I have raising two children? What I'd done wasn't fair. I couldn't leave. But I didn't know how to stay. It would've been better if I didn't stay. I didn't add any value to Kimmy, to Lizzie, or the new baby. The baby wouldn't even know me. Lizzie would barely remember me. Kimmy would always have her family.

I thought about options. I knew I had the means at home to deal with myself. I had my pick of three pistols sitting in my gun safe. But I also knew if I didn't get it right on the first shot, I would only make things worse. I was already a useless burden. I loved them too much to add a paraplegic father and husband to the load. If I did indeed do an inferior job, I wouldn't get a second shot at myself from a powerchair. But maybe I could drive into a pool. That would work.

The more I thought of ways to remove myself from the situation, the more I thought about Lizzie, about Kimmy, about the baby.

As the room got darker, I resigned to the fact that I didn't own my life anymore. I had given it to my wife and children. Whether I liked it or not, I knew that my life was no longer mine to take. I closed my eyes.

I heard the ocean. I saw the sunset. I knew where I was.

Dreaming was an art that I had once mastered. Before my surgery, I could go to certain places almost on command. I had a home—an escape from the waking world. I hadn't been to it in years. But that night I traveled there. To the house made with glass, concrete, and wood.

I found myself in my library. Two perpendicular walls of floor to ceiling glass afforded a panoramic view of the ocean. A Sota turntable rested on a table waiting to receive a record. I sifted through my vinyl collection. Soon enough, Erik Satie's Gymmopedie No. 1 filled the space.

I stood by the window, watching the muted tide lap up against the beach. His reflection appeared in the window as his voice broke through the music. I turned around to find my father sitting in my Eames lounge. Elbows on the armrests and his fingers interlaced, he asked, "It's been a while since you've been here. What are you doing?"

I replied, "I don't know. I just needed to be alone."

"And then what?"

"I don't know. How did you get here? Hey, wait, aren't you supposed to be dead?"

"Yup. Aren't you supposed to be alive?"

"I guess. There'll be too much blowback if I go with you. I just don't know how to go forward. I don't know what to do in life. I don't know what my next steps are. I'm scared I'm starting to feel like getting married was something I did to change my situation. I mean, I love her, but she didn't fix me. And I don't know how to be a father, how to be a husband.

"Kameron, I definitely wasn't an example of what to do right as a father and as a husband. You may have gotten married for the wrong reason, but you married the right woman. You have a perfect child with another coming to you. You want to know what to do? Look at them. You felt like you didn't have a life before them, you may feel like you don't have a life now. But look at your wife. Look at your daughter. They are your life. If you don't know what to do, do anything. As long as it's right, and as long as it's in their best interest. One day this setup of yours with the ocean, the house, the books, the music—it will be a reality."

"Dad, how do I know what to do? I want this life. I want this house. But I have no clue what road I should go down. I have no idea what I should pursue. I feel trapped."

"Son, you have a lot more people on your team than you think you do. Keep your mind open. Keep your heart open. You will get the answers you will get the direction you need. One of the most important things to understand in life is how to maintain balance in uncertainty. When you're stuck, just keep your cool. Answers will come. Direction will come. The doors will keep opening. You just need to trust us and walk through them."

"Okay. Wait, what do you mean *us*?"

"Your team."

Dad looked over at the turntable. The record stopped. "Might want to flip the record, Kam."

I walked to the record player. When I turned the record over, I looked behind me. The lounge chair was empty. I played side 2 and walked over to the chair where my father just sat moments before. I sat down and lay back. With my feet on the ottoman, I interlaced my fingers behind my head. I relaxed and listened to the music. The beach and the ocean were still visible under the moonlight.

Watching the tide roll in and roll out, I felt like I was starting to doze. The music suddenly changed.

An annoying xylophone overtook the room.

I opened my eyes to find myself lying in a bed, nowhere near an ocean. I looked over and saw Kimmy waking up to the sound of my alarm. I had a lot to think about on my way back to California.

Chapter 31

Descendant

May 12, 2016, 8:09 a.m.

Ten hours of labor were preparatory for both Kimmy and me. Ten hours prepared us to transition. A change from a child to an adult. A grown-up. That's how people would see us after we left the hospital, grown-ups—it was a daunting title. Where do you go if you are lost? A grown-up. Where do you go if there is a fire? A grown-up. Where do you go if you are in danger? A grown-up. Where do you go if you don't feel safe? A grown-up. Where do you go if you are broken? A grown-up. Where do you go when you need to cry? A grown-up. What happens when a storm causes the power to go out? A grown-up fixes it. What do you look for if you are scared? A grown-up. Grown-ups fixed everything for children.

For the last nine months, I knew the change would take place. The moment I couldn't come back from. There would be a point where I had to move forward as a parent. I would soon be someone else's grown up. I would be the person who fixed things, who protected, comforted, and reassured. But I had one problem. I knew I could be my own grown-up. I had been for the last ten years. But how could I do the same for someone else?

From the moment Kimmy's water broke, birth was imminent in her mind. She would have to bring a child into the world. After that, she would be a mother. I was sure it would come naturally to her. She had the innate ability to worry. To care. To be concerned. I knew she'd be fine. As her contractions came closer together, my mind and the room drifted farther apart. When Kimmy brought the child into the world, I would have to manifest a father for that child.

Kimmy and I anxiously awaited a future to be delivered to our hospital room.

The monitors spoke for our daughter—eager to arrive.

Kimmy yelled for her body—on the brink of rupture.

My head silently screamed for my mind—about to implode.

Over the course of ninety minutes, my wife pushed her way into a new role—my daughter's mother.

While holding Kimmy's hand, I awaited a transition. I expected one. A change from one stage to another. In all the movies, the parents had an instantaneous bond with the child. A love-at-first-sight bond between the parent and offspring.

As I waited, I found something else. Indifference. After indifference, followed horrible and piercing guilt. Why didn't I care? Why was I not in the moment? I should be in a spell of euphoric love, but I wasn't. The only emotion that hit me was fear.

I looked into Kimmy's eyes as she pushed. I still didn't get it. I tried again. I thought maybe there was something wrong with my heart. Was I not capable of love? I closed my eyes and searched for the circuit breaker. No matter how many times I flipped the switch up and down, I couldn't get the lights on. No power. In a few moments, I would have a child. Why didn't I care? Why wasn't I concerned about it? My eyes were startled open by the doctor.

Kimmy needed to get to the end quickly. The heartbeat dropped. Kimmy was nearly at her breaking point.

One…two…three.

She was in the final round. But I could see Kimmy fading. Though I didn't see how she, or anyone for that matter, could get through this, I encouraged her. She had to pull through it. I needed her to. Our daughter was starting to crown.

The doctor offered reassurance. Apparently, what was happening to my wife was just another day at the office for the ob-gyn. Time to push again.

One…two…three.

Kimmy yelled. Grunted. Screamed. She uttered a sacred language, only exclaimed during childbirth. It was a language that only mothers knew how to recite or comprehend handed down through an afflictive rite of passage.

One…two…three.

Kimmy summoned every remaining reserve of power. She exerted. It nearly broke her. I could only watch, helpless. Either she would break, or she wouldn't.

One…two…three…

The baby had been born. We had a daughter. We didn't know what to do with that reality. But we had it. Kimmy was barely there. She started to fade. The baby—she didn't cry. She was supposed to cry. She was also supposed to not be blue. She looked alien. I figured that was normal. But she most definitely was supposed to make noise. And she wasn't supposed to be pale.

The doctor summoned the nurses and a cart. I cut the umbilical cord. The baby and Kimmy were separated. The baby still hadn't made noise. Fluid. She started to drown. The medical staff continued to work—then we all heard it—a cry. A muffled cry. The baby was breathing. Barely.

I looked over at Kimmy. She was breathing as well. Barely. The baby lay in her cart struggling for life. My wife lay in the bed. Struggling for life. I was a husband. I was a father. Both of them needed me. The cart holding my baby started for the NICU. I couldn't be in two places at once. I looked at Kimmy as she lay in the hospital bed, trying to come back from a nearly fatal battle. She told me to follow our baby.

I floated down the hallway to the NICU, after our child. I saw her. Elizabeth. She was connected to a CPAP machine, a mask almost as big as her face provided her the means necessary to oxygenate her tiny body. The only thing visible on her face were her eyes, peering out above the mask. They searched for comfort. They searched for reassurance. They searched for safety. They searched for a grown-up.

They found me.

I connected with her eyes. Elizabeth was real. She was innocent. She was pure. She was beautiful. The world was behind those eyes. I couldn't lose her.

A nurse walked down the corridor. He was the only means of getting information about my daughter.

I flagged him down and asked a very grown-up question.

"My daughter is here. I need a status update. She was just brought here from the delivery room. Is she going to be okay?"

"Oh, yes. Mr. Parkin. Your daughter will be just fine. She just needs the CPAP for a few hours to get her used to the atmosphere. But don't worry, Daddy, you two will be just fine."

2018
August 4, Saturday, 10:00 a.m.

I stared through the windshield at the asphalt path leading to California. The road led to my future. It also led to accountability. I looked in the rear-view mirror at Lizzie. Her head rested on the side of her car seat. I watched as she fell asleep.

Lizzie's fingers slowly fell from her mouth. I looked back at the road and remembered when I was in a car seat—I never thought twice about my dad's competency behind the wheel. He was the best driver in the world. It was just the way it was. As a two-year-old, I had complete confidence in my dad to get through anything. It wouldn't be until much later in life that I realized he had no clue what he was doing.

With another glance at my daughter through my mirror, I started contemplating. It crushed me. Lizzie was completely asleep. She had enough faith in me (or ignorance) to trust me with her life. I, not unlike my father, was lost. It was up to me to provide a foundation for my daughter to build on. My father and I had a major similarity. We were both broken to a point where we didn't know how to be present for other people.

I couldn't let Lizzie get scathed the same way I had. I needed to get my shit together before it was too late, but I didn't know how. As we passed the Nevada—California border, I knew I didn't have much time. Kimmy fell asleep. I had the car to myself once again. The yellow lines on the road hypnotized me into deep thought.

I found Kimmy, but I hadn't found myself yet. I didn't have much time to find out who I was. I had yet to find my place in the world. I needed a place that I fit into. I needed purpose. It was time for me to find something that I believed in. something I was good at. The endless possibilities paralyzed me.

I needed answers. I needed direction. I needed something to trust.

We would be back home in a few hours. But was it truly home? Finding myself could happen with a miracle. At an arm's length, I had the only home that would remain constant. My loose ends in Utah would remain just that—loose. I left behind the pain. I felt a bit relieved. I didn't feel any obligation anymore. I only had a duty to the people in my car. I needed something though. A sign, a beacon, a message—something to steer me onto a path toward happiness. I couldn't be an office assistant for the rest of my life. But I didn't know of a better option. I needed help once again. Was it too much to ask for help twice? I fully acknowledged God's role in hooking me up with Kimmy. He worked in mysterious ways. He manifested my eternal companion by using my roommate. I needed to keep an open mind. The universe had to throw something at me. Something that I could grab with both hands, something with enough power to pull me out of my past and push me into a positive future. I was so close; I could feel there was some sort of vehicle waiting to pull me out. But it was so dark around me. Maybe I wouldn't find it. What would happen to me then? Maybe God would help me.

"Okay, God. So I know you're busy. You probably have a ton of voice mails on here. If you want to transfer me to someone else, that's fine. Maybe if my dad isn't doing anything, you can have him deal with me.

"Okay. Um, I think I asked for a bit more than I was prepared for. Don't get me wrong! Thank you for Kimmy and the kid. Not sure how we're gonna handle the next one. I guess we've kept Lizzie alive so far. It's your call. You must think the new baby is a good idea, so...

"Anyway, I'm starting to ramble—I don't mean to be one of those people who only come around when they need something, but I'm kinda stuck again. I can't keep doing what I'm doing. I need help. Again.

"If you can point me down the right road, I'll do whatever you need me to. I'm still broken. But this is different. I don't know what is wrong. The office is a great place. It's a great job, but I just don't know what I am doing there. I'm like a fish out of water. I can't do that forever. It was practically handed to me. So was the real estate training, but there's just something out of place.

"I know I need to find myself and stuff, but I found Kimmy first. I wasn't even supposed to live, remember! But this all happened, now I have a wife, two kids, and a dog, but I'm failing. I am failing hard. You know how many times I groan your name every day! Things aren't really going all that smooth.

"I gotta find out who I am. And I don't have the time to search. I don't know where to look. I know it's a bit early to be cashing in my life-lines.

"But if this is my last chance to get help from you, I think the smartest way to use it is to get to the point where I can help myself.

"I won my dream family—with your help. I love them more than anything, more than myself. I need a way to keep my dream family after I wake up. I need to find a way to support them, to take responsibility and provide. A man provides for his family.

"Now I'm not saying it's your fault, but I am in way over my head with this. I didn't prepare for it. When everyone else was worrying about the next phase of their life, I zoned out. I didn't think I needed to pay attention or worry. I was going to die, right? I was going to be up there with you! I was busy partying and waiting for the end. Now I don't know what to do. You brought them to me. Now I need you to bring me to me.

"There has to be a purpose for all of this, but I'm not seeing it. You know it's true, what they say about your warped sense of humor.

I'll trust it, but I can't leave my family hanging. I don't want them to look at me with disdain. I don't want to fail them. I just don't know how to succeed. I'll do whatever it takes. I hope at some point this will slow down. I can't play catch-up forever. I have a breaking point.

"All I need is a career that makes sense, God. You're the big man. You control things, or at least you can point things out so I can control things. I need a revelation. Give me that, and I will do the rest.

"All-righty, I'm going to hang up now. In Jesus's name, Amen."

Chapter 32

Violent Delights Have Violent Ends

2018

September 20. It was two months to the day that Dad was rushed to the hospital. Kimmy and I were getting ready for bed; it had been a long day. Kimmy got in the shower when I heard the noise coming from my nightstand. I looked over to find that Mike Burton was once again trying to reach me by phone.

I looked over at the bathroom door. Steam from the shower had already begun to leak out of the bottom. I took a breath and exhaled as I walked over to pick the phone up.

"Hey, son, how are you doing?"

"As well as I could be, I guess."

Mike sounded a bit drunk. He was slurring a little, and it seemed like his mind was distant. I could hear him muttering under his breath. "Don't be sorry, Mike."

"What was that?" I asked.

"Oh, nothing. So, Kameron, I just want you to know that even though your dad is gone, you will always be a son to me. I love you, and I'll take care of you because Mike is gone, because your dad is gone. And I want you to remember that it's not your fault. This shit just happened. You didn't cause it. No one caused it. It's not a problem. It's just shit that we have to get through! We got to get through it because if we don't, it is going to catch up with us and kill us. And you can't let this kill you too, because it was an accident! I mean it just happened. For no fucking reason. And that's all I have to say about that. But it's not your fault, and I think you're a pretty standup guy. You got a wife. And you got the baby. And you've got another baby too. So don't fuck it up. Because it's really hard to come back from if you fuck it up. There's no just coming back. There's no fucking second chance. This is all you've got. And you just need t-to you know, just live. So your dad dying and what happened wasn't just for fucking nothing, you know? Yeah, so I just wanted to call and say you're a good guy and don't fuck it up and I'm sorry."

"Thanks, Michael. That's a lot of good life advice there for me to digest. But what are you sorry for?"

"Oh god. Kameron, I don't know! I just...I just want to say that you're a good guy. I wish things were different, and I wish that this didn't happen because it's like all over. He was the love of my life. And I had to fuck it up. I'm so sorry for everything that you've been through. It's just not fucking right. But before you judge your father, you need to stop. You haven't walked an inch in his shoes. You haven't walked an inch in my shoes. You don't know what happened that night. It's just...it's...just the way that it happened. And no one can do anything to change it. And that's just the way it is. All I'm trying to say is you're a good guy, and I love you, and I hope that you're going to be okay because it's going to be okay. I'm not gonna say I'm sorry. Don't say you're sorry, Mike! you're going to be Okay! All right. I'm kind of tired, so I'm gonna be going to bed pretty here soon. Good night, and good night to your wife. Okay. All right. Bye."

"Thanks for talking, Michael. Bye." I hung up. It was the first time Mike Burton had contacted me since the funeral. Mike Burton was no more sober today than he was at the funeral. It was nice to know that I wouldn't have much reason to ever contact him again.

2018
September 21, Friday, 2:00 p.m.

I had three hours left of an unusually long workday. I kept my cell phone on at work but always kept it on vibrate. I only answered the phone for a select few people.

When I felt the pulsing on my right thigh, my hand instinctively rushed to cease my phone. I pulled my phone out of my pocket and saw the caller ID. My heart began to race. Why would *she* be calling me?

I answered, "Hello?"

"Hello Kameron."

"Oh, Hi. How are you?"

"Well," she sighed. "Things can't get much worse."

"Oh, I'm sorry to hear that. Is there anything I can do?"

Silence took hold of the phone line. "What happened? What's wrong?"

Mrs. Burton paused for a moment, then exhaled. "It's Mike. They found him in his hotel room last night. He's dead."

Opposing emotions held me captive. I didn't know how to react. I didn't know what to say. I didn't know anything. My mind lay on its back, just below the surface of a sea of potential reactions. If I moved at all, I would be forced to grab onto one and swim with it. But I didn't know which reaction was appropriate. For a time, I chose silence. Silence was the only reaction that I could take back without consequence.

On the inside, my head was screaming. Could it be? Mike Burton might just finally be gone.

"Oh no. When? How? Did—did he leave a note? Anything?"

Even though I didn't have a problem with Mike Burton killing himself, I thought that the bastard at least owed me an explanation or a goodbye.

"They found him early in the morning today at around two. He was in his hotel room. They found about a dozen liquor bottles. Maybe some pills. And no, there wasn't a note. But he was very paranoid when he went to the hotel. He was staying with us and decided that he needed some time just by himself.

"He went and got a hotel room about three days ago and he seemed very paranoid the last week. He kept saying, 'They're going to get me. They're going to find out. I can't go to jail. I just can't go to jail.'

"He seemed convinced that the police would somehow for some reason link him to Mike Parkin's death, but I don't know, it was all just nonsense."

Then I realized that I had indeed received a goodbye even though I didn't know at the time.

"I just talked to him last night. He seemed fine. A little drunk. But not suicidal."

"I know. I guess he couldn't take being without your father."

"Mm-hmm. I'm so sorry I am at work right now. I'll give you a call back later, okay?"

"Okay, Kameron, love you."

"Uh-huh. Buh-bye."

I ended the call. Leaning back in my chair, I didn't know what to do. My mind fought with my body over which emotion to put in play. I sat at my desk, stupefied by fear.

I'd been submerged in the waters of distrust and wariness ever since Mike Burton attached himself to my life. Mrs. Burton's words had broken a cuff around my ankle. I had all but run out of air. I had already affirmed that I would drown below the surface.

I barely noticed that I'd been cut away from Mike Burton when I started drifting away from the weight of him. I found freedom. For the first time in a long time, I could kick without him pulling me down toward the dark.

I looked up. The light of the surface became brighter—light overtook the darkness. I fought harder to get to the top. Below me, Mike Burton lay in a pitch-dark void.

I broke through and felt the air and light. My soul drank in the air. I'd been starved of breath for so long that I struggled to breathe at first. But I knew he was gone. He was no longer a demon that vied for my failure. The monster that nearly defined me had vanished. He had sunk to a pit where he would never be seen or heard from again. He had no power over me.

He had scarred me. But we were now in two different worlds.

I left my desk and ran for the door. When I got to my car, I sat behind the wheel and looked through the sunroof up at the sky. It happened. It came at a tragic price—but it happened.

Mike Burton was finished.

I broke down. I cried. I yelled. I laughed. I took hold of a new reality. One where I could be the kind of father I wanted to be. I started my car and sped out of the parking lot. I reached the house.

I drove up the hill and saw her playing on the deck. My daughter. My daughter that would never have to see the incubus of Mike Burton again. I ran up to Lizzie and saw her perfect smile.

"Hi, Daddy!"

"Hello, Lizzie."

"Come play with me, Daddy."

"Daddy would love to."

Chapter 33

Forensics

2018
October 2, Tuesday, 2:00 p.m.

I needed to get a hold of their computers. Maybe there were clues on them. Maybe there were texts exchanged. I called him, desperate. He had all their stuff in storage.

He answered. "Hello?"

"Hey, Mr. Burton. It's Kameron. I know you are busy, but you said earlier that you were able to recover their phones and computers? I was wondering if you could send them to me through FedEx. I have an account with them. I'll cover shipping. You don't even need to pack the stuff. They will take care of it all." I was trying to maintain my poker face. I needed this.

He responded, "Oh yeah, we got a computer and a tablet. No phones though. We can't figure out how to get into them. But you're good with computer stuff. Sure, I will get that off to you as soon as I can. And, Kameron. I know that we have lost them, but we haven't lost each other. We will always be there for ya. You don't have to call me Mr. Burton."

"The grandkids call me Pop-Pop."

2018

December. The box from Pop-Pop finally arrived. It was a mess. Mike Burton's iMac. Dad's tablet. A DVD player. A bunch of cables. I got the essentials out. The trackpad. The keyboard. The mess of cables had to come out too, as they were ensnaring the iMac and keeping it hostage. The yellowed keyboard had a piece of masking tape on it, written on the back was "michael parkin." I rolled my eyes. Mike Burton was dumb as a rock when it came to internet security.

I unpacked the box. More would come from Pop-Pop. When I had all my father's possessions from his storage unit, I would burn Mr. Burton. His son was no longer a scourge that affected me. Soon, my life would be free of the Burtons—though they did leave a mark.

I took the ten-year-old iMac out of the box Pop-Pop had FedExed to me. Everything was labeled. Dad was obsessed with labels. The keyboard was labeled. The bottom of the computer was labeled. After five minutes of waiting in prayer the computer booted. I clicked on the password field, entering Dad's name according to the label on the back of the keyboard: "michael parkin."

Success. I was in the account. I waited the entire month of November for that Pandora's box to arrive from Utah. I opened the web browser. The idiot who owned the computer before had never cleared his browsing history. The most recent Google queries confirmed my suspicions.

> "Statute of limitations for manslaughter."
> "Homicide sentences."
> "Trauma that doesn't show up on autopsy."

An obituary sat open on the desktop. According to the modified date, my father's obituary was the last thing the computer was used for. I ripped the computer's power supply cable from the wall.

Murder hit me.

Chapter 34

The Path Forward

2019

When I unplugged the computer, I noticed the typewriter Dad had given me from beyond the grave. The machine sat in the corner unused, with a sheet of paper loaded into it. I took the boat anchor and placed it on the desk. It seemed to be looking at me, almost as if it were asking me something.

I flipped the power switch. The machine greeted me with a low hum coming from the electric motor. I sat back in my chair, listening to the hum. Looking at the typewriter. The sound was soothing. Isolating, in a comforting way. Like my head was just below the waterline of a pool.

A single sound pierced through the hum. It was as if it came from right behind my ear. His voice captured my mind with only two words.

"Write it."

I pressed the first key. The augmented power of the electric motor flung the typebar into action, tattooing ink into the multipurpose copy paper I'd pulled from the printer. The sound hit my ear from the platen being struck.

The sound told me the words I was forming were mine. I could share them to whomever I wished. With the added confidence from the typing machine, I started firing off keystrokes. Letter after letter.

Texts turned into words. Without being audited by a computer, not having a grace period to waver from commitment. There they were. Being flushed out of my head where they had been for so long. Having remained dormant for my lifetime, appearing as if my thoughts held their potential energy for over twenty years without losing power.

There was no telling who they were going to knock down. Or who they would push forward. But they were printed into the world.

The only certainty was that my experiences were now outside my own head. My dirty laundry was exposed. Someone had to pay for the Laundromat.

End

About the Author

Kameron Parkin lives in southern California with his wife and two children. Through the process of publishing his memoir, *Of Substance*, Kameron broke into the field of professional writing to engage in his lifelong passion—storytelling. Kameron continues to search for and develop stories that illustrate the human condition.

His first book paved the way for Kameron Parkin to fulfill what he feels is his purpose, to facilitate the sharing of emotion. Both gritty and sweet, Kameron sees the worth in all feelings and experience.

Kameron Parkin was born on May 2, 1995, in Nephi, Utah. The only child of Michael and Stacey Parkin, Kameron began a struggle with epilepsy at age fourteen. At age seventeen, after being given a year to live, he sought medical treatment at Harbor View Medical Center in Seattle, Washington. A successful operation enabled Kameron to return to Utah for college. There, he met his wife, Kimberly. After studying history education, Kameron left college and moved to California. Soon after relocating, Kameron began his career as a professional author.

Visit www.kamparkin.com for more content
and other titles by Kameron Parkin

CPSIA information can be obtained
at www.ICGtesting.com
Printed in the USA
FSHW012301010420
68725FS

9 781643 348704